5-Star Review by Readers' Favorite

Ashley McDonough has successfully broken down the principles of Operations and Supply Chain Management in a guide called *Operations and Supply Chain Management Essentials You Always Wanted to Know*. It is an in-depth book, which does more than explain the concepts. McDonough takes an example of the production of pairs of scissors through Planning, Control Systems, Procurement, Purchasing, Sourcing, and Manufacturing. The author then introduces us to principles of quality and brings us through the logistics of distribution of the scissors. There is wonderful continuity told in plain language while bringing us through an example from the first phase through logistics.

Each concept is easily explained in non-technical language. The specific examples bring the concepts to life. One caution—this is not a quick read. To fully understand and appreciate it, the reader needs to pay close attention to how the examples illustrate each section. It is well worth the extra time, as the author carefully lays out the process from start to finish, and makes operations management and logistics quite understandable to the reader. The descriptions of Theory of Constraints (Chapter 4), Total Quality Management and Continuous Improvement (Chapter 5), and Logistics (Chapter 6) are excellent explanations of manufacturing, concerns, quality concepts, and logistics.

Operations and Supply Chain Management Essentials You Always Wanted to Know by Ashley McDonough is a valuable book for anyone interested in first learning the concepts and also for those wanting an overview as well as explanations of specific concepts. It is excellent in its use of an example, specifically following a pair of scissors from start to finish. This makes it much easily understood by the reader.

– Randy B

D1592795

Operations And Supply Chain Management

Essentials You Always Wanted To Know

ISBN-10: 1-949395-24-3

ISBN-13: 978-1-949395-24-2

Library of Congress Control Number: 2019943484

This publication is designed to provide accurate and authoritative information in regard to the subject matter covered. The Author has made every effort in the preparation of this book to ensure the accuracy of the information. However, information in this book is sold without warranty either expressed or implied. The Author or the Publisher will not be liable for any damages caused or alleged to be caused either directly or indirectly by this book.

Vibrant Publishers books are available at special quantity discount for sales promotions, or for use in corporate training programs. For more information please write to bulkorders@vibrantpublishers.com

Please email feedback / corrections (technical, grammatical or spelling) to spellerrors@vibrantpublishers.com

To access the complete catalogue of Vibrant Publishers, visit www.vibrantpublishers.com

What experts say about this book!

Operations and Supply Chain Management Essentials You Always Wanted to Know by *Ashley McDonough* is a valuable book for anyone interested in first learning the concepts and also for those wanting an overview as well as explanations of specific concepts. It is excellent in its use of examples.

I think the book would be valuable for a junior level undergraduate class in SCM. Maybe a course that all business students should take to get a clear understanding of the concepts of the overall supply chain. The efforts to put together a relatively succinct text on OSCM is appreciated.

> – **Wendy L. Tate, Ph.D.,**
> **Professor of Supply Chain Management, University of Tennessee & Co-Editor in Chief Journal of Purchasing and Supply Management**

The book is nicely written and I will recommend this book as an useful reference text book. For someone who doesn't have a lot of time and is looking for a quick point of reference to Operations and Supply Chain Management, this is THE book for them. This book is perfect for students at undergraduate and graduate courses. If you are a PhD student, you may want to resort to the classical books.

> – **Rameshwar Dubey, DBA, Ph.D.,**
> **Associate Professor of Operations Management, Montpellier Business School & Editor – Journal of Supply Chain Management System**

What experts say about this book!

I had the opportunity to read *"Operations and Supply Chain Management Essentials You Always Wanted to Know"*. Supply chain and operations management are technical concepts and usually very difficult to be expressed on paper in a communicative way. This book is able to do that by adopting "user-friendly" and "not too technical" language, without losing the rigor that characterizes these disciplines.

Following the SCOR model, the book navigates through the main concepts of planning, sourcing, making and delivering. It concludes with concepts about supply chain strategy & design and futuristic supply chain trends. The ability to communicate such a broad content by condensing intense information and integrating it with industrial examples & real cases is a plus of the book.

In synthesis, the author succeeds in making operations, supply chain management and logistics quite understandable to a non-technical audience, without losing the OSCM technical soul. The pair of scissors metaphor, particularly, is a great example (used from start to finish) that I will definitely propose to my students!

> – **Andrea Patrucco, Ph.D.,**
> **Assistant Professor of Supply Chain Management,**
> **The Pennsylvania State University**

Table of Contents

About the Author

Ashley McDonough is a Supply Chain and Finance professional who holds an M.B.A from the Hong Kong University of Science and Technology, one of the top M.B.A. programs in the world. She also holds a Bachelor's degree from the University of Minnesota, with an emphasis in Supply Chain, Operations Management, and Economics.

Ashley has worked in various Supply Chain functions including planning, manufacturing, quality, logistics, continuous improvement, research and development, and project management. She has over 5 years of experience in large corporations as well as start-ups, in the United States and across Asia. This exposure is spread across various industries, including electronics, agriculture, FMCG, banking, retail, and apparel. As a firm believer in making complex supply chain concepts understandable, and a desire to share her experiences, Ashley has served as a corporate trainer on digital transformation and continuous improvement, both with emphasis on the implications to the Supply Chain.

Her diverse work history prepared her to write her first published piece as a contributing author to Food Safety for the 21st Century, highlighting her experiences working with dairy and packaging start-ups in Sri Lanka on their quality and environmental plans. Her exposure in the developing world gave her an understanding of how supply chain practices can be modified or simplified given the context in which they are being applied.

By complementing her professional experience with a passion for writing, Ashley hopes to share with others the complexities, challenges, and excitement that comes with working in the Supply Chain in a simple, yet practical way that is easy for anyone to understand.

This page is intentionally left blank

Preface

When I have talked to colleagues and fellow classmates about Supply Chain in the past, it is often within a matter of seconds that their eyes glaze over, as they mentally move on to far more exciting and "sexier" things than anything Supply Chain. To be honest, I can't hold it against them, as I was in their shoes just a few years back – I didn't even know what "Supply Chain" or "Operations" was until well into my university years. I certainly didn't believe it was anything of relative importance until I started my career in a Supply Chain Management development program for an agriculture company.

Initially I was drawn to the planning and project management aspects conducive to a desk job, but as I saw the day to day fires that needed to be put out, things got more and more… interesting. People needed to be flexible, play nice, and get creative to make things happen for the company to function on just a basic level. Everything from catching birds in a warehouse, to figuring out how to dispose of 500 pounds of moldy cheese required an army of managers and line works alike. Stationed in rural Wisconsin was not at all where I had envisioned myself at 23, but it was different (a good different) in that it was totally unique from what I could have ever expected. Perhaps the biggest benefit of this role was that it gave me exposure that was a mile wide, with a glimpse into how various functions operated. That being said, could you claim that I am a jack of all trades, but a master of none when it comes to Supply Chain? Absolutely. This very critique however gave me the inspiration to write this book - to share my experiences in each function, and to showcase the collaboration necessary to make Supply Chains actually link together.

At the heart of the various roles and departments I worked in were the people working third shift from midnight to 8 a.m., those planning production orders on their vacation, and the manager getting up in the wee hours of the night by their supplier in Vietnam. These activities often go unnoticed in our society unless you are actively involved in them. Many of the people I have come across in these roles have inspired me, and propelled me forward in my career. As a thank you for the lessons learned and doors opened – especially with living and working abroad early in my career - this book is a tribute to those whose work happens behind closed doors. They are the guts that make the fancy advertisements and new product launches happen. The least I can do is share their stories with you in hopes that you too will receive the benefits of their knowledge, humor, and grit.

My intent is to show you the interworking and puzzles that come along with functioning in an efficient Supply Chain, but not to change your opinion about Operations and Supply Chain functions within the modern world (no, you do not have to like your Supply Chain counterparts telling you they won't get you your delivery on time). Instead, I will show you why Supply Chains matters, and how everyday decisions in the Supply Chain can have magnifying effects that you may not even realize. Although paying attention to the Supply Chain can enhance a company's competitive position, or increase consumer satisfaction, just as importantly it gives us to access everyday products and services that we need, such as clothing and food. I guarantee that you will want this access to continue - and Supply Chains are the ones that make it happen. Even as your desires and preferences evolve, the Supply Chain is there to make your wildest demands seemingly realistic, or even possible!

Throughout our story, I pull in experiences from the developing world, corporate America, and from projects that I worked on internationally. You will get a fundamental overview, but note that it is an overview biased towards my collective experiences, so some areas are not covered as in depth as others in the interest of cohesiveness. What this also means, however, is that you will get rich and original examples that highlight why you might want to pay attention to what the Supply Chain and Operations functions are up to. This book is not deeply technical, or really technical at all, as my goal is not to give you a Supply Chain degree. You won't be an expert on the topic, but you will be dangerous enough to fool your colleagues into thinking you may have actually worked in a Supply Chain role. Who knew?

Now open your mind (and your eyes if I have lost on Supply Chain already), and be prepared to learn about the world of Supply Chain Operations through a company making a product you probably never knew was so complicated – a pair of basic scissors.

This page is intentionally left blank

Introduction – Supply Chain in the Modern World

In an ever-evolving and technologically advancing world, companies are faced with meeting changing consumer preferences. As the marketplace develops, processes, procedures, strategies, and practices within an organization must also adapt to meet both a company's internal strategy as well as market demand. Many of the adaptations and adjustments that are required to help businesses stay competitive fall under the Supply Chain and Operations functions. By partnering with other departments in the organization, the supply chain is strategically positioned to efficiently and effectively deliver the desired value of the firm, while optimizing the firm's resources in the process.

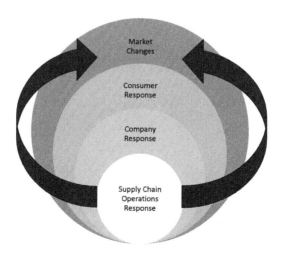

As Supply Chain Operations within an organization adjust to ever changing trends, regulations, and consumer demands, inefficient management of such change can have catastrophic results, both financially and in terms of reputation. As we will see throughout the course of this book, the way in which an organization adapts its Supply Chain Operations to the external factors that are outside of its control, can serve as a means for significant and sustainable business success. By the end of this book you will be able to answer the following questions regarding concepts in the area of Supply Chain Operations Management:

- *What is Supply Chain and Operations Management and why is it important?*

- *What are the key functions within this field, and how do they interact with one another and the broader business?*

- *What are the responsibilities and decisions that managers in each functional area think about?*

- *How will disruptions in the Supply Chain impact the business world and our lives going forward?*

- *What are the practical applications of the knowledge gained around Supply Chain Operations?*

Chapter 1

What is Supply Chain and Operations Management?

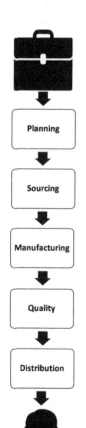

Planning

Sourcing

Manufacturing

Quality

Distribution

If the need for effective Supply Chain Operations is so critical, what does that mean? How can one accomplish it and what should you be concerned with? The Supply Chain involves the activities within the company that bring products and services to life. It includes the flow of goods, both in the form of raw materials and finished products, how those goods are stored, and how they reach customers. It is developed based on a company's business plan, of which the Supply Chain can then turn into a reality. In doing so, supply chain teams are often responsible for balancing supply and demand, putting out fires, and ensuring the company is running smoothly.

What are Benefits Delivered by Supply Chain Operations?

Aside from market response, Supply Chain Management is an important consideration for managers. To demonstrate why modern managers are paying increasingly more attention to Supply Chain operability, let's look at a few other ways the Supply Chain can enhance business performance.

- **Competitive Advantage**   A Supply Chain can become a competitive advantage in countless ways if it allows a company to operate in a more favorable way that competitors are not able to match. For example, are you able to offer products in an area where none of your competitors can? This may be a geographic advantage in terms of your distribution reach. Can you manufacture the same product faster than others in your industry? This is an example of a competitive advantage driven by a company's manufacturing process. This creates a more favorable position for the firm and thus results in greater profitability for an organization.

- **Customer Satisfaction**   It is no secret that customers can have high expectations of the products that they purchase. There is an expectation that the desired product can be delivered at a specific price, in a specific location, at a specific time. For any company, there are costs associated with how you provide such availability and service to your customers. Without effective Supply Chain Operations, hiccups such as inventory shortages or delayed service requests can decrease customer satisfaction and even lose customers to a competitor altogether.

1

- **Efficiency**   Few areas within an organization can improve efficiency quite like Supply Chain Operations. Everything from reducing the amount of material input required for a necessary product to the number of people required to produce the product will increase efficiency and can be easily traced to impacts on the bottom line, as you are achieving more with less. Walmart is a famous example for Supply Chain Operations efficiency – by harnessing new technologies they have been able to improve the flow of information throughout the company, and reduce the amount of inefficient and excess inventory.

- **Cost Cutting**   Perhaps the most commonly recognized form of Supply Chain Operations benefits, Cost Cutting, is closely related to efficiency. Because there is direct contact with the product or service being offered, Supply Chain Operations has the ability to impact cost decisions, such as decreases in the purchasing costs of product inputs, decreasing the cost of production, and eliminating expensive product attributes. Organizations are usually very cost conscious and work to deliver their desired value in the most cost-effective way possible, without sacrificing quality.

These are just some of the many benefits that can be delivered through Supply Chain Operations. Each benefit requires cooperation and collaboration with other departments within the organization to achieve such synergies. Just as important however, is that each functional area within the Supply Chain Operations category coexists with one another to deliver the company's desired strategy.

Functional Areas Within Supply Chain Operations

1

The Supply Chain Operations function is broken into a series of different departments throughout an organization. It is important to distinguish early on the difference between the terms **Supply Chain** and **Operations** because although both traditionally fall under the responsibility of the Chief Operating Officer (COO), there are subtle differences in what each area is responsible for. The key differentiating factor is that **Supply Chain** traditionally focuses externally around functions such as planning, sourcing and distribution that are impacted by environmental factors. Alternatively, **Operations** focuses on the internal processes within a company such as manufacturing and quality, and how these can be best controlled. What is critical to realize, however, is that these two areas overlap substantially, and are dependent on one another. As such, we can use the term **Supply Chain Operations(SCO)** to describe this standalone area of management.

We can see the various functions that will fall under the Supply Chain Operations umbrella. As the name suggests, the functions fall within a "chain" where each is "linked" and dependent on the one prior as well as after. It begins with internal strategy development, and ends as the business is able to deliver value to the market. Each "link" has a critical role to play in delivering such value.

Business Strategy Development:

Each company will develop a direction for its business that

will be used to meet customer needs, achieve business goals, and remain competitive in the market through differentiation. Strategy discussions are traditionally determined at the highest level of an organization, which will then flow down from top management to all individuals in the company. With a strategy in place, steps can be identified, such as new product development or geographic expansion, to reach desired goals. These goals may include financial targets, or how quickly the company wants to grow. In addition to an overall business strategy, sub-strategies may also exist for specific areas of the value chain, such as a marketing strategy or research and innovation strategy. The key strategy considerations that we will focus on will be in relation to the organization's supply chain strategy.

Planning:

With a supply chain strategy in place, a company must estimate what they think their performance will be. This is often considered forecasting, and will be used to predict how many units will be sold. Once this is determined, requirements for raw material inputs, production time and capacity, as well as storage requirements can be determined. It is important to note that "units" of product are not always tangible items. For example, music, software downloads, and e-reading material may have planning requirements in how a company would plan for delivery to customers. Developing an approach to planning will be further discussed in Chapter 2.

Sourcing:

Once a plan has been devised, the company must then "source" the materials that will be needed to produce their

1

desired goods or services. This includes purchasing the raw materials from vendors that will be used as inputs to the manufacturing process. It may also include human capital that is required for assembling products, or a media firm that can assist in producing digital content. Sourcing involves selecting which resources to obtain, how much will be paid for those resources, when they will be delivered to the company, and who will supply them. Strategic relationships are thus very important for a company to define, in order to ensure consistent and reliable inputs into the Supply Chain.

Manufacturing:

The inputs gathered in the sourcing process are then utilized at the manufacturing stage. Manufacturing processes are defined based on the product being created, and the desired attributes of that product. How much or how many units to produce of that product is determined in the planning stage. Various manufacturing methods can then be used to shorten production times, hold less inventory, or produce less waste in creating the product. These decisions are all factored into the manufacturing design. The output of product is thus a function of the constraints in the design of the manufacturing process.

Quality:

To ensure that products meet customers' needs on a consistent basis, Quality Management systems often are put in place. These outline the procedures for producing products that are safe, meet customer criteria, and consistently deliver the same product. Quality procedures often outline the steps needed to meet regulatory requirements and comply with international product standards. Quality is usually the last line of defense for a company's product before it is sent out to the market.

Distribution:

When a product has been produced and passed all quality checks, it can be sent to consumers. It may be sent via truck, plane, mail, or rail at different times and to different places. How a product is delivered to customers may depend on factors such as the company's business model, where there is consumer demand, time of year, shelf-life of the product, and countless other factors. Overall, distribution is the way in which the good or service is transported from the company to a marketplace of customers.

End Consumer:

As a result of the various functions within the supply chain, a consumer will see a finished product on the shelves at a local retailer or available for purchase at an online marketplace or e-store. Rarely will the end consumer realize the level of planning, organizing, and diligence required to deliver even the most basic of products. Driven from the strategic perspective, a product will have built-in attributes designed to meet customers' needs and thus warrant cause for purchase. It is at this point that we would see the Supply Chain pivot if consumer's needs are not met and a product is not being purchased. This may circle back to the strategic decisions that drove the justification for producing the product in the first place.

This general overview outlines the critical functions within the supply chain. Throughout the course of this book, we will dive deeper into each functional area to better understand its

1

specific importance to the company's operations, the considerations that professionals in each function should be concerned with, and how they contribute to the overall synergy of the Supply Chain and product delivery.

The concepts we have addressed thus far may seem hypothetical at this point, so to better demonstrate the interworking of Supply Chain Operations, we can use an everyday product to showcase what challenges may arise and how these can be managed. As you will see, problem-solving is a key element in making the Supply Chain sustainable and functional for day-to-day operations.

SCO in Action - CTC Scissor Co.

For the sake of simplicity, let's refer to a relatively basic product to demonstrate the concepts and workings of Supply Chain Operations: a pair of scissors. As a common household item used to cut paper, tape, and other miscellaneous materials, this may seem like a relatively trivial product; however, we will quickly see how internal and external changes derail the process of bringing something as simple as a scissors to life, using a fictional company – Cut the Cord Scissor Co. (CTC).

CTC Scissor Co.

CTC has been in business for over fifty years as a leading provider of scissors for offices and households alike. They have a strong customer base, and good financial performance. They distribute across four regions –North, South, East, and West. There

1

are only three major competitors offering a comparable product across all regions combined. CTC is responsible for each step within the supply chain, including procurement of materials and manufacturing at their factory, which has 80 employees.

The scissors itself is made up of three basic components – two stainless steel metal blades, each with a handle, and a pin or pivot that is used to hold the scissors together. The product is used for basic purposes across different consumer groups, and is the only product that CTC offers. In reality, this would be unlikely, given the overhead costs associated with producing a product -- it would be more common that a scissors company, with a scissors factory, would produce many variations of scissors, but in the interest of isolating a specific Supply Chain change, we will assume this individual product is able to sufficiently justify CTC's operations.

Figure 1.1

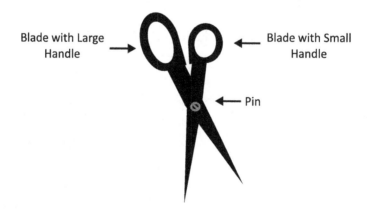

Demand for the CTC scissors is currently 1,000 units annualy across all regions. This is supported by five customers, with individual demand represented in the table below.

Table 1.1

Region	North	East	South	West	
Customer	A	B	C	D	E
Demand (units)	400	96	240	114	150

Despite fifty years of success, CTC has seen a decline in sales of these scissors over the past three years, and is contemplating changing this product to better align with customers' preferences. This would be a strategic decision that would send ripples across the company. We must therefore examine the implications of such a decision and how different functions within the Supply Chain could respond. The aim will not be to advise what is the correct course of action, but rather to highlight the trade-offs that Supply Chain Operations managers must analyze in order to move the organization forward.

Although Sales and Marketing and Product Development are not our key focus area, we must take the time to understand these functions and how their priorities and decisions may impact Supply Chain Operations within CTC. We can see from the following diagram how information from consumers flows into the organization, is processed, and is translated in order to develop a meaningful organizational response.

Figure 1.2

1

Voice of the Consumer   Meaningful Insights   Organizational Response

Sales and Marketing Impact

Sales and Marketing serve as an integral part of the feedback loop, alerting the rest of the company about changing consumer needs and new trends in the market by both existing competitors and new entrants. This often presents challenges to Supply Chain Operations due to lack of understanding of what constitute practically feasible and financially viable changes that can be made to keep up with the evolving market conditions.

The Sales individuals within the organization interact directly with customers. Through this communication, they are better able to understand the customer's needs and brainstorm ways that these needs can be met. Typical responsibilities of Sales Managers include developing relationships with clients, gaining knowledge about the local market, defining the differentiating factors of the company, and offering customized solutions to meet consumers' needs. They are also responsible for generating new business, which is often done through lead generation and engaging potential business clients.Sales Managers would provide critical insight into why the sale of the CTC scissors has

1

been declining. After discussing with the Sales Managers in each of the four regions, you may learn the following:

- Customer A is interested in switching to scissors that have a more comfortable grip, as they use the scissors to cut cardboard boxes throughout the day, which puts a lot of pressure on their employees' hands. Due to concerns over employees' health and concerns of arthritis, their organization has decided that the CTC scissors will need to be replaced. A competitor, Sadie's Scissor Shop, is able to offer them a more ergonomic scissors at a 25% price increase from their current product's selling price, which we will assume is the same price as the CTC scissors.

- Customer E, a wholesale office supplier, is not able to sustain their sales of the CTC scissors and will be decreasing their annual demand from 150 units down to 50 units within the year.

- A company in the South region, Connie's Cutting Corner, has been identified as a new potential customer, but will only purchase units at a 5% discount off the current price. They are also interested in purchasing scissors that have a jagged edge, which make decorative edges when cutting paper.

As this information is gathered from customers, it is relayed back to the broader organization for its response. Marketing Managers can contribute meaningful insights into how to respond to such news and developments.

Although the role of a Marketing Manager, a key marketing function, often varies in companies based on the size of the organization, company goals, and the company structure, individuals in this role often look at key market segments, an exercise known as Segmentation, to understand how to grow business with these customers and what changes will need to be made to do so.

One commonly used framework to evaluate if you have the right product, or marketing mix, to satisfy these customer segments is called the 4P's of Marketing. The 4P's include analysis of the product, price, promotion, and place to understand how you can plan a successful offering to your customers. We can use our example of CTC to understand what each of the 4P's analyzes.

- **Product**   Are you offering the correct product that meets your consumers' demand? Products can be either tangible, like the scissors in our case, or intangible, such as a service. What benefits does your product offer? Does your product have the right features? For example, if CTC was selling a scissors for cutting hair, the hairdresser may require a sharper blade, as opposed to a school purchasing scissors for children in the classroom where a dull blade may be required to prevent injury. In the case of Connie's Cutting Order, the demand for a scissors with a decorative edge calls for a product that adds value to their consumers that a regular scissors would not.

- **Price**   Price is the amount of money that a customer is willing to pay for a product. It is based on how much they value the product and its attributes. If the product is seen as too expensive, consumers may not purchase it, and retailers such as Customer E may not be able to effectively sell the product. For something as common as a scissors, consumers may see little value in the product, so it needs to be priced lower in order to sell. Price can also depend on distribution and production costs or the price of competing products.

- **Promotion**   This may include advertising, sales tactics, special offers, and store promotions. These methods of communicating to customers are the marketing function. Could a promotion be offered through Customer E's retail business to promote sales of the CTC scissors? This would likely need to be subsidized by CTC. If Customer E has too much inventory of CTC scissors that they are unable to sell, this is one way that they could induce customers to purchase more of the product.

- **Place**   Place, or Placement deals with how the product is distributed to the end customer. Are customers buying the product through a big box retailer or at a specialty store? Can it be purchased online or delivered? In the case of an office purchasing the CTC scissors, do they order supplies directly through a preferred vendor of office supplies, or do they simply pick it up on their way into work? These decisions all depend on the nature of the product. For example, perishable items may be more difficult to purchase through online retailers, or a large printer may not be available for pick-up. The product, price, and promotion all will dictate where the product can be sold.

Given these considerations, individuals in the Marketing function will work together to develop a marketing strategy that aligns with overall company objectives. In light of their analysis of the market, can they make a decision on whether they should change the CTC product to better align with consumer preferences? Should they keep their existing scissors, but expand to offer two different variations? What about the information that the Sales Managers provided? We can't quite answer these questions just yet. Another perspective that is required must come from Research & Development and will help in assessing the appropriate action for CTC and what the implications will be for the supply chain.

1

Product Development Impact

Product Development, commonly known as Research and Development (R&D) functions are the innovation center for many companies, creating new products as well as supporting existing ones. Product Development divisions often pair engineers, scientists, project managers, and academics together to explore new product or service opportunities for a business. They may follow news and developments specific to their industry. For example, an R&D scientist at a financial services firm may want to understand developments in block chain, whereas a scientist at a food company may be concerned with new food additives and changing regulations. Product Development is there to help respond to such changes and works closely with the supply chain to understand current capabilities, areas for improvement, and aspirational goals. Given the many moving parts at play, Product Development may design an Innovation Strategy to parallel the marketing strategy of a company.

In our example of CTC, Customer A and Connie's Cutting Corner both expressed interest in new products that CTC does not currently offer. How could CTC understand what would be required to offer these products to their existing and new customers? Most Product Development companies participate in a product development process, often called a Stage Gate, to understand the viability of a new product or enhance existing ones. A hypothetical Stage Gate process is shown below, where each set of activities must be validated before it can pass through the "Gate" to the next stage.

1

Figure 1.3

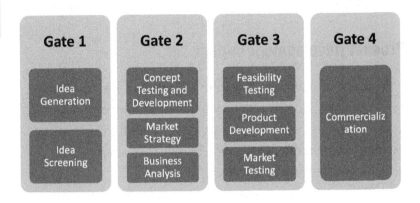

You can see that as ideas are generated, they must be justifiable for other stakeholders of the organization as well. Supply Chain Operations Managers are the voice at the table to communicate what these decisions may mean for Planning, Sourcing, Manufacturing, and Distributions functions – all of which we will discuss throughout the book. This is a highly collaborative activity across the organization, with the owner of the process, or the "Gatekeeper" residing in Marketing or Product Development roles. This responsibility is dependent upon organizational structure and how the company chooses to assign responsibility for such functions. Oftentimes, the biggest question to answer is if it is time to innovate, and if so, how will it be done, when, and who will do it?

CTC's Decision

With an understanding of how Sales, Marketing, and Product Development impact new and existing products, let's circle back to the information obtained from the market by the Sales Managers. We can critically evaluate each product request to understand how CTC can respond. Let's list some of the considerations that may arise. Note that each decision may impact the other, and the firm will need to evaluate each collectively in order to decide their course of action.

1. Customer A wants a scissors with a more comfortable grip and can order them from Sadie's Scissor Shop at a 25% higher price.

    This is a question of new product development, and is a cross-functional decision. Some possible considerations of each department are outlined below.

    Sales: Customer A is 40% of the current demand for the CTC scissors. If their needs cannot be met, they have claimed that they will switch to a competitor and are happy to pay the 25% higher price for a scissors with a grip. How do we know that they are serious about their willingness to switch suppliers? The reality is you wouldn't be 100% sure. Could they be saying this to add pressure on CTC to innovate? With an established relationship and distribution in place, Customer A may find it easier to stick with CTC.

    Marketing: Does the grip align with the customer segment that CTC aims to meet? Will a scissors with a grip be a consistent and sustainable product demanded in the future? If so, will it be distributed in the same way? What other product attributes should be considered, if any? If Sadie's Scissor Shop can offer at a 25% higher price, will CTC be able to produce the new scissors at a competi-

1

tive price?

Product Development: *CTC has not had any innovation over the past fifty years. Creating a new type of scissors may present some challenges as there will be a substantial learning curve. The existing product has proven reliable, and requires little maintenance, giving the R&D individuals time to manage new projects. Quick designs have proven that scissors with a grip could easily be made with modifications to the manufacturing process and purchase of additional raw materials.*

After thorough debate and alignment with the company's strategy, it is decided that the new scissors with a grip will be produced in addition to the existing CTC scissors.

2. Customer E, a wholesale office supplier, is not able to sustain their sales of the CTC scissors and will be decreasing their annual demand from 150 units down to 50 units within the year.

    When sales decline, there are a number of factors that could be at play. Given a decrease in their purchasing, this will require deeper analysis to understand why the change occurred. Potential factors include a decrease in market size within the region of Customer E, the West, or new competitors of Customer E entering the market of which CTC is unaware. Is there a new potential customer that CTC doesn't know about? There are countless factors that could contribute to this change, but with Customer E accounting for 15% of the annual demand, CTC will need to understand the root cause of the change as soon as possible. This may result in a new initiative undertaken by the sales staff, or an adjustment in the distribution strategy. At a cross functional level, there are no actions to be taken at this stage.

1

3. Connie's cutting corner is a potential new customer willing to purchase traditional scissors at a discount, and is interested in purchasing scissors that have a jagged edge, which make decorative edges when cutting paper.

   As we did in the first scenario, let's weigh out some of the considerations of each department.

   Sales: Connie's Cutting Corner is a traditional big box retailer that spans all four regions. They have indicated their demand for traditional CTC scissors would be nearly 400 units annually – the same amount as the largest existing CTC customer. With demand from Customer E dropping, new customers could be critical for maintaining and even expanding business operations. Although they are purchasing at a discount, the volume they purchase may make up for it. Although the decorative scissors are not a requirement for gaining their business, it would help to access more customers in new segments and reduce the number of suppliers that Connie's Cutting Corner needs.

   Marketing: Let's say that Connie's Cutting Corner does meet the target market for the traditional CTC scissors – great! If there is a way to reduce the cost of manufacturing the scissors to offer at the 5% discount without sacrificing product attributes, it would be a way to gain a greater share of the market that CTC may not reach through the current distribution network to date. If not, there may be some promotions that could be devised to incentivize Connie's Cutting Corner to stock CTC scissors. In terms of

1

the decorative scissors, this hits at a much smaller, niche market that CTC has not entered before. Without confidence around these consumers' preferences, it does not make sense to devote resources to a decorative scissors. Although research could be done to understand the craft market, this market segment does not align with the overall company or marketing strategy.

Product Development: *After initial feasibility testing, it would require substantial production modification to make a scissor blade with a different edge. If Connie's Cutting Corner purchases additional units of the traditional scissors, there may not be capacity in the existing factory to produce traditional scissors, a scissors with a grip, and a decorative scissors. It may be too much innovation to manage all at once. The scissors with a grip is much more technically feasible, as it simply requires changing out the handle. That is not to say that just because the decorative scissors are dramatically different it cannot be done; however, given the amount of time required to bring the scissors to market, it may be more than can be undertaken at this point in time.*

Given this discussion, it is decided that there will be further investigation into reducing production costs for the traditional CTC scissors by the requested 5%. The decorative scissors will not be pursued.

The analysis outlined above is not an exhaustive representation of the discussions and considerations that may be addressed in an organization. Rather, this outlines in simple form what the broader organizational decision making process might be. That is not to say that the Supply Chain Operations voices are not included in the front end of the decision making process – they absolutely are. What our discussion leaves out are many of the implications of such decisions, which we will spend the rest of this book discussing. We will understand just how Supply Chain Operations are involved in these decisions and how they are equipped to respond.

1

This page is intentionally left blank

Chapter 2

Planning and Control Systems

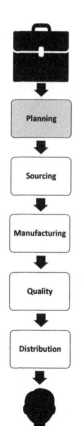

In the previous chapter, we learned what supply chain is, why it is important, and some of the functional areas that fall under Supply Chain Operations. We then learned about the organizational decision making process using the fictional company, Cut the Cord Scissors Co. The following changes were decided:

1. A new product, a scissors with a grip, will be brought to market to meet the demands of existing and potentially new customers.

2. Connie's Cutting Corner is interested in purchasing 400 units annually. This is contingent upon a 5% discount that CTC is unsure if they are able to offer.

In addition to regular business operations, CTC must plan accordingly for such changes.

Without a plan in place, customers may not be able to get their products on time, or the products may be unavailable where they want to buy them. What would go into such a plan--what are the factors that CTC needs to consider? We will answer each of these questions throughout this chapter as we look at the various elements of the planning function.

2

In this chapter, we will evaluate the following:

• *How companies plan and make production decisions*

• *Tools that planners use to be successful*

• *How materials, people, and facilities work in harmony to produce products*

• *Considerations for allocating and managing inventory once it is produced*

Before we dig deeper, it is important to understand some key concepts that impact the Supply Chain Operations activities within an organization.

• **Executive Sales and Operating Plan**   Above all planning and scheduling functions is the Executive Sales and Operations Plan. This balances the supply and demand decisions, and links the operational decisions back to financial plans to provide a clear path forward for the Supply Chain Operations of the organization. It serves as a roadmap for how the company strategy can be carried out, and is agreed upon cross-functionally. From here, detailed plans can be made.

- **Lead Time**   This is the amount of time needed to make a product from the first point of initiation until the process is complete. For example, manufacturing lead time may be the amount of time that is takes to produce a product from when the facility receives the order. Take CTC, for example. Let's assume that it takes two days to make a complete pair of scissors. The overall Lead Time for the scissors may be closer to four weeks as it would include the entire process from when the order is placed, to when the materials arrive, to its production, and then distribution to customers. Lead times are determined by a number of factors including product complexity, order placement, and contract arrangements between companies and their customers.

- **Safety Stock**   To prevent a company from running out of product that is available to ship to customers, they often keep a number of "safety" units on hand that are finished products which can be sent in extenuating circumstances to customers when there are fluctuations in supply and demand. In the case of CTC, they may average a demand of 83 scissors per month. They may choose to keep a safety stock level of 10%, or about 8 pairs of scissors on hand to ensure that they are not missing out on sales to customers. Issues that may require use of safety stock could be defective production runs, lost shipments, or acceptance of late customer orders that are outside the standard ordering window.

- **Service level**   Companies and their customers may enter into purchasing contracts that often stipulate service levels. This is the number of units ordered that could be filled using inventory on hand. Service levels measure

2

performance against predetermined service expectations. For CTC, this may include metrics such as a 98% on time delivery rate, or 99% fulfillment rate of all orders. Depending on the extent of the customer relationship, companies will usually work very hard to meet their service level targets, as these metrics are often the basis for how further business is determined.

Master Scheduling

Within any manufacturing company, planning is key for operations to run smoothly. Planning ensures that the correct number of raw materials, personnel, and other resources are needed to create the necessary number of products. This determination is then populated into a master schedule that outlines when and where the necessary resources will be required. This drives individual Material, Production, and Inventory Plans which we will discuss later in the chapter.

Plans are put in place to better prepare for business operations, but a series of factors can often alter such plans, and thus must be accounted for in the planning process. To develop a Master Schedule, we must first know how many products are required and when. This process starts with the generation of a forecast. Forecasts are determined using a variety of methods. These can be both quantitative and qualitative, and may rely on information from historical performance, market research, expert opinion, regression analysis, customer surveys, and time series methods. Because the number of actual customer orders may not be known before the products would need to be produced due to the necessary lead time, forecasting can reduce some of the uncertainty.

To illustrate forecasting, we can refer to the CTC scissors. Let's say that Customer D orders their 114 pairs of scissors throughout the year. Historically, from January to October, they demand 9 units per month, and 12 units per month in November and December. If, for example, CTC requires all orders over 10 units to be placed two weeks in advance, but the lead time for a scissors is 4 weeks, then in November and December, CTC would need to estimate how many pairs of scissors they should produce. In an ideal world, customers would be required to place orders for products in excess of the lead time needed to make the product so that a company would know exactly how much to produce. However, if we look at plane engines, for example, that have lead times that span multiple years, we can quickly see that customers may not know their demand for a product so far in advance.

Predetermined forecasts are used to help estimate what demand may be, which is then validated through actual customer orders. With a forecast to guide us, we can generate a concise demand plan that tells us how much of each product a consumer will demand and when. Demand for products is often variable and can be impacted by factors such as seasonality.

Seasonality   Fluctuations in demand may occur throughout the year, depending on seasonal factors. We saw this in the example above with Customer D.

Starting with our demand plan, we then must balance it with our supply plan and how much product already is made. Each product that a company produces will likely have a safety stock level that is kept. When orders come in, planners can choose to either fulfill them through existing inventory, or make the product from scratch, but under normal circumstances the safety stock level must be kept. If there is not enough on-hand inventory, the product will need to be manufactured.

With a demand and supply plan in place, the necessary process has occurred upon which the master schedule can be developed. A summary of the planning steps that feed the Master Schedule is below.

2

Figure 2.1

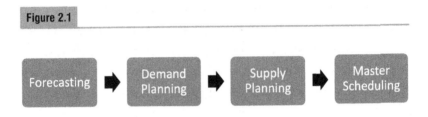

The Master Schedule will take each of the given inputs into account to generate sub plans around Material Resource Planning, Enterprise Resource Planning, and Inventory Planning. As we dig deeper into each individual plan, let's recount some details of CTC and the traditional pair of scissors that they make, to develop the Master Schedule:

- CTC currently has one manufacturing facility with 80 employees. We can assume that they run one 8-hour shift, with a minimum of 30 employees working at a given time. They can produce 25 scissors per hour, at a rate of 1 pair every 12 minutes using 5 different manufacturing lines.

- Let's also assume that it is currently December and we are planning for March of the following year. Because it there is a four-week lead time for producing the scissors, we would need to plan production for March no later than January. Resources, such as raw materials and labor, will also need to be obtained prior to production, which creates a need for planning so far in advance.

- **Demand**   Forecasted customer demand is outlined below. Note that customer E previously ordered 150 units from CTC, but now will order 50 units annually. Demand is also relatively constant for the sake of demonstration, but may swing dramatically for companies in industries that are heavily impacted by seasonality

2

Table 2.1

	Jan	Feb	Mar	Apr	May	Jun	Jul	Aug	Sep	Oct	Nov	Dec
A	30	30	30	50	30	30	50	30	30	30	30	30
B	8	8	8	8	8	8	8	8	8	8	8	8
C	20	20	20	20	20	20	20	20	20	20	20	20
D	9	9	9	9	9	9	9	9	9	9	12	12
E	8	8	8	4	4	4	4	2	2	2	2	2
$\sum$	75	75	75	91	71	71	91	69	69	69	69	69

- **Supply**   A safety stock level of 8 pairs of scissors must be kept at all times. We can assume that there will be this level of safety stock at the start of the year in January. Based on the production plans in place for the first months of the coming year, anticipated supply levels are outlined below. We can assume that all units are held at a central warehouse and can be distributed to all customers. Note that in reality, distribution networks can be quite expansive and often extend internationally. It is not always the case that available product could be distributed to any customer at a cost-effective price.

2

Table 2.2

(In Units)	Jan	Feb	Mar	Apr
On Hand Inventory	10	8	8	50
Safety Stock	8	8	8	8
Available Inventory	2	0	0	20
Demand	75	75	75	91
Production Required	73	75	75	

Note that in January, production occurs only for the number of units needed to exactly meet supply. In reality, it may be more efficient or cost effective to produce more units during a production run, and hold these as excess inventories. Although these would incur costs to store, what we call Inventory Holding Costs, cost benefit analysis can determine if this is a more practical approach.

Now that we know the Demand and Supply requirements of CTC for the traditional pair of scissors, we can determine the Master Schedule for March. For simplicity, we will plan on a monthly time horizon, when in practice, Planners may plan for weekly or even daily time frames.

A minimum production of 75 units will be required to meet-forecasted demand for March. Because we can see that in April there will be demand for 91 units, and we are running exactly at the required safety stock level, we will choose to produce 80 units. One key factor in this decision is that if we look where this demand is coming from, it is predominantly from Customer A, who requires 50 out of 400 annual units, or approximately 13% of their annual demand to be delivered in April. In preparation, and to ensure that they receive their order, CTC can err on the side of caution and produce extra units that will be added to "On Hand Inventory" if the units are not needed.

2

Oftentimes Planners have software that will do these calculations for them, factoring in customer orders, inventory adjustments, and production changes in real time. Automated alerts can be built into such systems to alert a Planner when modifications to the plan are needed. This is where the "Control" element comes into play, as software can often manage complex, multi-layer plans for various products at multiple different manufacturing sites. For an individual planner, even the smallest change to these plans could be catastrophic without an automated system to suggest ways in which products can become available.

With this Master Schedule in place, the downstream planning tools – the Material, Enterprise, and Inventory Plans, can be generated.

Figure 2.2

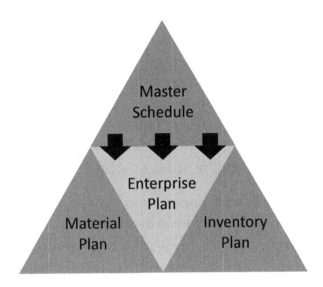

Because these are dependent on the Master Schedule, it is critical that there is alignment up front and visibility across the Supply Chain Operations Functions in order to turn these plans into reality.

Material Resource Planning

Now that we know how many units we will produce in March we need to ensure that we have the raw materials required to make the required pairs of scissors. Let's refer back to the traditional scissors that CTC currently makes.

Figure 2.3

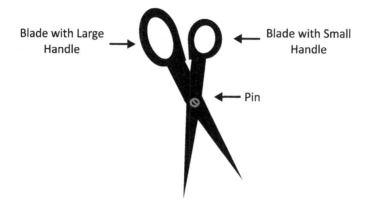

Blade with Large Handle →   ← Blade with Small Handle

← Pin

2

The traditional scissors are a relatively simple product with only 3 components. Both blades are manufactured by CTC out of stainless steel, and the pins are purchased from an external supplier. Each of the materials, the pin and the steel, will be listed on what's called the Bill of Materials for the product. A Bill of Materials is defined when a product is created, and outlines in detail what individuals in the Sourcing and Procurement functions need to purchase in terms of raw materials for the product. There may be inventory on hand for each component, or there may not. Each individual material will likely be purchased separately, and often from multiple suppliers.

Looking ahead to March, we can develop the Material Resource Plan based on demand and on-hand inventory. We will assume that each pair of scissors requires 0.25 units of stainless steel and one pivot. Given the number of units we want to produce, we can work backward to understand what the material requirements are. Be reminded that CTC decided to produce five additional units in March in preparation for additional demand in April.

2

Table 2.3

(In Units)	Jan	Feb	Mar	Apr
Production Required	73	75	80	91
Pivots Needed	73	73	80	91
Stainless Steel Needed	18.25	18.25	20	22.75

As with on-hand finished goods, there may also be on-hand raw materials that can be used. As with safety stock for finished goods, there .also may be safety stock for raw materials which are reflected in the tables below, following the logic that the proper amount of finished safety stock is 8 pairs of scissors per month.

Pivots:

Table 2.4

(In Units)	Jan	Feb	Mar	Apr
On-Hand Inventory	175	94	13	
Safety Stock	8	8	8	8
Available Inventory	167	86	5	
Pivots Required	73	73	80	91
Purchase Requirement	0	?	-75	

After production in February, there will be only thirteen pivots available for production in March. If there is a production requirement for 80 finished pairs of scissors, that means that CTC will be short 75 pivots. As a result, a Materials Planner would work with the Sourcing and Procurement functions to ensure that a supplier of pivots would be able to deliver a minimum of 75 pivots by the time they are required to be used in production.

2

Stainless Steel:

Table 2.5

(In Units)	Jan	Feb	Mar	Apr
On-Hand Inventory	100	81.75	63.5	43.5
Safety Stock	2	2	2	2
Available Inventory	98	79.75	61.5	41.5
Steel Required	18.25	18.25	20	22.75
Purchase Requirement	0	0	0	0

Because there was built-up steel inventory at the beginning of the year, there is not a requirement to purchase any steel, even going into April. A reason for such a high raw material supply at the beginning of the year could be from lower production demand toward the end of the year, or if there was an advantage from a sourcing perspective. For example, some raw materials may have long lead times, such as 6 months, that would require a manufacturer to purchase large quantities in advance. Suppliers may only sell in bulk or offer discounts for purchasing at certain times. There are various reasons why this could occur, many of which we will touch on in depth in the following chapter.

CTC now has a Master Schedule, and knows what materials need to be ordered to support the required level of production. The next step is to develop the production plan.

Production Resource Planning

2

Many considerations need to be taken into account for planning the actual production of a product itself. These include routing production orders to the appropriate facility through capacity planning, pushing orders to the factory to start a production run, and scheduling employees. Once production begins, Planners will follow up with how the plan is going, and make adjustments as necessary.

Because CTC has only one manufacturing facility, there is no need to decide which facility will carry out the production run. In reality, large-scale companies may have multiple manufacturing facilities that can produce their products, each with different capacities and capabilities. Companies can also outsource the production process altogether using a contract manufacturer, which still requires the same planning steps. Because CTC has only one manufacturing facility, this limits the amount of capacity that is available for production.

To demonstrate just one element of the actual production planning process, let's look at the labor resources that would be required by CTC, using the month of March as our planning horizon as we did before, where we are planning to produce 80 units. If 25 scissors can be produced per hour using 5 different manufacturing lines, that means that it takes 12 minutes to make an individual scissors. This also means that, under these conditions, there need to be 960 minutes of work across these 5 lines to produce our required 80 scissors.

Figure 2.4

	Line 1	Line 2	Line 3	Line 4	Line 5	
Number of Employees	6	6	6	6	6	30
Scissors per Hour	5	5	5	5	5	25

80 Scissors Needed / 25 Scissors per Hour = **3.2 Working Hours Required**

If the production facility wants to create the traditional CTC scissors using the existing 30 employees working on the manufacturing line, it will take just 3.2 hours to produce all of the scissors required for the month. This poses a challenge for employees who are planning to work a full 8-hour shift, and indicates that the manufacturing facility is dramatically over capacity and may have the option to serve as a contract manufacturer for other companies, or alternatively have fewer employees. One potential solution may be to operate on fewer manufacturing lines. This will open up the possibility to use those lines to produce other products.

Let's say CTC decided to operate just one manufacturing line. From our knowledge of CTC's manufacturing rates, we can calculate that if a scissors takes 12 minutes to manufacture, and we need 80 scissors, the same 960 minutes of total scissor production

2

are required. How that production is allocated may be a different story. A single line producing at the same rate of 5 scissors per hour would require 16 hours of production. Whereas there were 30 employees required to staff all 5 lines, now there would need to be only 6 employees to staff the individual manufacturing line. The diagram below demonstrates the revised scenario.

Figure 2.5

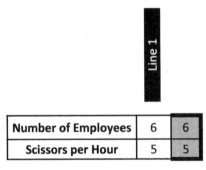

	Line 1	
Number of Employees	6	6
Scissors per Hour	5	5

80 Scissors Needed / 5 Scissors per Hour = **16 Working Hours Required**

This allows the 6 individuals to work 2 full 8-hour shifts, which may be beneficial from a management and resource efficiency perspective. It would require training and onboarding of fewer employees, eliminate some overhead costs associated with Human Resource Management, and give manufacturing workers a more consistent and reliable schedule. We could dig far deeper into staffing requirements and their implications, but for our purposes we will simply use this example to learn how just one area of production planning may be analyzed.

With production plans in place, it is time to consider what to do with finished products once they are complete. This brings us to our final planning topic that we will discuss – Inventory Planning.

Inventory Planning

2

When planners look at where to put inventory, they often consider warehouse space that is onsite at the manufacturing facility, or warehouses within their distribution network. Inventory-holding decisions often have financial implications, so planners must align their company strategy with key metrics such as service level to balance how much inventory to hold and where to hold it. It is key to remember that there are both finished goods and raw materials inventory that need to be stored. It is best practice to keep these held separately, and depending on the nature of the product, such as food items, it may even be a regulatory requirement.

Perhaps one of the most important metrics for planners to consider when making inventory decisions is called Carrying Cost. This is a measure of how much it costs to "carry" an item based on factors such as space, manpower to move it, risk of the product becoming obsolete or damaged, and loss of the product if it can no longer be found among the other inventory. In addition to Carrying Cost, there are also Ordering Costs associated with placing the actual order, and Shortage Costs for procuring materials that are not available when needed.

Along with these costs, there are various benefits to holing inventory as well. Holding inventory can provide a supply buffer in the case of unexpected orders and increased demand. It allows for product delivery and the avoidance of lost business. It can also optimize efficiency in transportation if you want to send bigger shipments to customers at a given time. Finally, it protects against seasonal fluctuations that introduce uncertainty into the inventory planning process.

2   To understand some of the financial considerations associated with inventory, we can look at two critical concepts in the realm of inventory management - Last in First Out (LIFO) and First in First Out (FIFO).

- LIFO is a principle that assumes the most recent item produced will be sold first. If a company's inventory costs are rising, this may be a better strategy as the highest value items are considered sold right away, as opposed to holding on to them.

- FIFO alternatively assumes that the first product that was produced is the first to be sold, which aligns with typical inventory management practices. If inventory costs are going down, typically FIFO is better to use.

This is just one factor to evaluate the level of inventory to hold. Another strategy is to define not only your safety stock level, but your reorder levels for specific units of inventory as well. From the graph below, we can see that over time inventory fluctuates for a specific product.

Figure 2.6

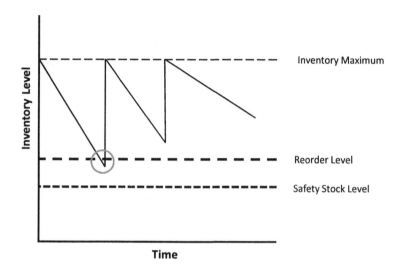

2

Before inventory falls below the safety stock level, more product may be ordered or produced to ensure that there is adequate supply. This is known as the Reorder Level and is shown by the red circle. On the flip side, there may be an Inventory Maximum that a company would define to prevent excess inventory. These levels can be defined for each individual product, with rules built into an electronic system that will signal when the Planner needs to take action relative to an inventory level. Again, these decisions will be made on a strategic basis and at a cross functional level.

CTC Implications

How do we apply this broader understanding of how the Planning and Control Systems function to CTC and their new initiatives? We can evaluate the necessary steps and considerations from a Planning perspective.

2

1. A new product, a scissors with a grip, will be brought to market to meet the demands of existing and potentially new customers.

   a. A forecast will need to be determined. As this product is new, there may be more guesswork involved to generate a demand plan that is realistic and captures consumer demand for Customer A until actual orders are received.

   b. There is no existing supply of product, so it will need to be determined how far in advance production should begin in order to meet forecasted demand. Production times can be estimated by the initial feasibility studies conducted.

   c. The new product will have different material requirements that will have to be sourced in advance. This may involve new suppliers for the additional materials.

   d. As the product has not been made before, the time an capacity required may fluctuate during initial production runs.

   e. Manufacturing workers will need to be trained on how the new scissors is produced. This may require additional staffing.

   f. Depending on the packaging and distribution strategy for the product, optimal inventory levels will need to be determined for both raw and finished goods. Whereas before, only one type of scissors was distributed, now there will be multiple products that need to be organized in a warehouse environment.

2. Connie's Cutting Corner is interested in purchasing 400 units annually. This is contingent upon a 5% discount that CTC is unsure if they are able to offer.

   a. Without knowing if demand will actually increase for the traditional scissors by 40%, it is very difficult to create an accurate demand plan. CTC will need to create assumptions around each scenario (demand either increases or remains constant) to determine what demand level they should plan for. Fortunately, they have significant excess capacity that would allow them the option to produce the additional scissors in their current factory.

   b. In terms of supply, this is an existing product that the facility already makes. They could start producing additional units in anticipation that Connie's Cutting Corner will become a customer, but if this doesn't happen, they may incur substantial inventory holding costs.

   c. This uncertain demand and supply feeding the Master Schedule trickles down to impact material requirements, production resources, and inventory plans. Ultimately, the company will need to keep a close eye on the conversations with Connie's Cutting Corner and develop contingency plans in case they come on board.

2

Based on simply the planning function within the Supply Chain Operations field, we have witnessed how these departments can contribute significantly to making an organizational change a reality. Supply Chain and Operations managers would bring the ideas we have outlined to the table during the strategic decision-making meetings, as well as during steps throughout the Stage Gate process. Everyone, from those responsible for the Executive Sales and Operating Plan to Product Managers, may have a say in how to handle such changes.

2

To summarize, in this chapter we have done the following:

- *Identified considerations that individuals in Planning roles must consider.*

- *Demonstrated that Demand and Supply balance to generate a Master Schedule, which then feeds planning decisions around materials, inventory, and production resources.*

- *Emphasized the importance of cross functional engagement in the planning process to ensure that the Executive Sales and Operating Plan can be carried out effectively.*

Next, we will analyze how Sourcing and Procurement functions provide the necessary resources and inputs for such plans.

Chapter 3

Procurement, Purchasing, and Sourcing

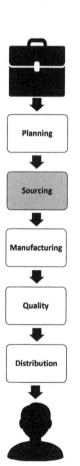

From the moment a customer places an order, a company must get to work in either allocating the product from finished inventory or manufacturing it. What we saw in terms of planning is that preparation may need to happen before the company knows how many actual orders will be placed. This preparation includes obtaining the necessary goods and services from suppliers that will be required to meet the order demand. As a result, the Procurement functions initiate the start of the Supply Chain.

In this chapter, we will dive deeper into the Procurement, Purchasing and Sourcing procedures to learn the following:

- *When and how a company may choose to procure production inputs*

- *How suppliers can be evaluated and selected*

- *The difference between traditional and strategic sourcing approaches*

3

Let's use our traditional scissors from CTC to introduce some of the concepts that we need to be aware of for Procurement. For our scissors, we discussed the Bill of Materials (BOM) in the previous chapter, which would tell the Procurement functions what raw materials would be needed for producing a specific product. The BOM would be developed when the product was first launched. In the case of our scissors, although there are three components, two of these (each of the handles), are made from the same raw materials. As a result, we see a BOM with one less raw material item.

Figure 3.1

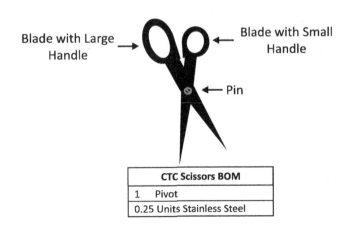

CTC Scissors BOM	
1	Pivot
0.25 Units Stainless Steel	

The BOM outlines just the *physical* materials that are required; however, services may be required to source as well. Common examples of service inputs that are sourced include Business Processes or Information Technology (IT). This brings us to an important distinction between what is considered Direct and Indirect Sourcing.

- **Direct Sourcing or Direct Spend** is for materials directly used for the company's business generation, which in our case is a physical product – the scissors. For a grocery store, this may be food items to sell, or in the case of a chemical company, the actual chemicals. These go into the end products that generate revenue for the company.

- **Indirect Sourcing or Indirect Spend** relates to the internal costs for the company that are required to keep it operational, but that will not be sold to generate revenue. This may include costs for administration, utilities, facilities, office supplies, and travel expenses. Although these are not materials going into the product, they are critical for production. For example, electricity would be required to manufacture our scissors, but, a customer would not be buying the electricity that was consumed to make the scissors, but rather the scissors itself. This may look different if for example you were the electricity provider where your product was actually a service offering instead of a physical good.

With an idea of what items we would need for CTC, let's look at the actual Procurement process itself. **Procurement** is the end-to-end process of purchasing direct products and services. **Sourcing** is a subset of Procurement that involves finding "sources" or suppliers from whom to buy the required products. **Purchasing** is the physical order and payment of goods. From the diagram below, we can see how each of the Procurement functions relate.

Figure 3.2

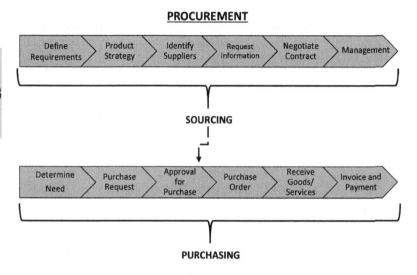

The Sourcing and Purchasing functions intersect when an actual order is going to be placed. With approval to make the purchase, it must be determined where to make the purchase. Requirements are identified for the product or material that will be an input for the finished product, so that the Sourcing team can then develop a strategy for procuring that item, and identify suppliers. With additional information and negotiation, a supply agreement may be reached with a contract put in place. Continuous purchases can then be made with the supplier under the same supply contract. This contract will be managed on an ongoing basis by the Sourcing department. This streamlines the purchasing process because as purchase orders (the physical requests to the suppliers) are approved, the actual purchases can be done relatively seamlessly. The Sourcing and Purchasing functions shine light on how important it is to select suppliers that can meet your purchasing needs.

Supplier Decision Criteria

In an international marketplace with large and small-scale producers, each with varying levels of technical ability, it may seem like a daunting process to find the right supplier that would meet a company's needs. Fortunately, the steps in the supplier selection process help us understand what Sourcing professionals evaluate and how they pick a supplier. The steps in the supplier selection process are as follows.

Define Criteria   What are the company's current sourcing needs? What are you looking for in a supplier? What are the expectations and how do they align with overall company strategy?

Define the Process   How will these suppliers be found? Will they be involved at trade shows or in industry groups? Will they be domestic or international companies? An overall industry analysis is helpful to understand who the major players are.

Request Bids   Based on the criteria and process identified, which companies will you reach out to? What information do you hope to get from them? This often goes beyond simply pricing discussions.

Evaluation   Offerings from various suppliers must

be evaluated collectively to determine what attributes are of the most value to the company. How technologically advanced are you hoping your suppliers are? Are you confident in the management team they have in place?

Selection   Once you have identified suppliers that your company would like to work with, a contract can be put in place around a number of attributes, including, for example, minimum order quantities, delivery performance, discounts, and pricing terms.

Performance Monitoring   Once a contract is in place, performance can be measured against your agreed-upon terms. Does the supplier meet your expectations? If not, what can be changed? Will you continue to purchase from them in the future?

There are many factors that feed into the supplier selection process. It can be helpful to develop a Supplier Evaluation Matrix to understand the strengths and weaknesses of each supplier relative to the criteria you have defined. If we refer back to the traditional UTC scissors, you will recall that one of the components on the BOM is a pivot. We will assume that the pivot is a critical part of the scissors (as it holds the handles together), so as a result, a quality pivot that is a balance between affordable and reliable is the strategy for sourcing the pivots and thus selecting a supplier.

We can develop a matrix around the four current suppliers of these pivots. Each supplier is given a score of 1 – 5, with one as the worst and 5 as the best rating for each evaluation category.

Table 3.1

	Pete's Pivots	Pivotal Point	Hank's Hardware	The Pivot Palace
Management Team	5	3	5	4
Long-Term Potential	4	3	3	2
Capability	4	5	1	3
Price	2	4	1	4
Quality	4	5	4	4
Financial Stability	5	4	5	2
Delivery	4	4	1	3
Interoperability	3	2	1	2
Total	31	30	21	24

We can see from a strict numbers perspective that Pete's Pivots ranked the highest in overall attribute score on our matrix, with 31 points. Does this mean that we should purchase all pivots from their company? Not necessarily. This tool is a means to start the discussion around which supplier to select. Let's compare Pete's Pivots to Pivotal Point, the company with the next closest score of 30 points, to understand how these suppliers match up.

In looking at the Management Team, it is important for a company to have partners that they can work with closely. There are a number of reasons why Pete's Pivots could rank higher – does the team have a close relationship with the individuals at Pete's? Are they easy to work with and willing to collaborate? Often times, a supplier's performance is tracked using a scorecard. Does management respond favorably to feedback discussions? This could definitely impact the rating assigned to their team.

Next, we can compare <u>Long-Term Potential</u>. Does CTC see a longer-term relationship with one supplier over the other? Do they have more confidence that Pete's Pivots will be a reliable supplier, and around for a long time? If so, this could eliminate headaches down the road. On the flip side, a supplier like Hank's Hardware that may not specialize in pivots, or where pivots are a minute fraction of their business, may not stay in the pivot business and could be unreliable for a long-term commitment.

<u>Capability</u> is an interesting factor to evaluate, especially for products that are not very advanced or technically involved, such as a pivot. That may not be the case for products in the electronics or machinery industries. This category does however, incorporate technical and manufacturing capability to address the overall strength of a company's operational ability.

<u>Price</u> is often the key factor that comes to mind when evaluating sources of supply. There is a delicate balance, however, between getting a product for an affordable price and ensuring that the product still meets your quality targets. Here, it may be that Pete's Pivots are more expensive, and are thus given a low score for this attribute. Pivotal Point on the other hand, was given a higher score on price, which could be due to the availability of promotions, or cheaper prices when purchasing with a bulk order discount.

Closely related to pricing discussions might be those around <u>Quality</u>. This could involve everything from the actual quality of the products delivered, to defective product, to the quality systems and checks that are in place at the company. The price vs. quality debate is usually a discussion of trade-off during this type of evaluation. You can see that Quality only varies by a factor of 1 between Pivotal Point and Pete's Pivots, but Price has a difference of 2 points.

Financial Stability is an interesting and often challenging attribute to evaluate. It is rarely known how well your suppliers are doing from a financial perspective, but there are usually indicators that may point to financial trouble. Possible signs could include requests for earlier payments to manage cash flow, or late shipments. Of course, these examples do not *always* indicate financial distress, but are rather signs to be aware of. If there are any concerns about the financial stability of a company, it is important to conduct business with them cautiously.

3

Delivery times are usually outlined in existing or potential supplier contracts. How often are these deliveries late, or fulfilled with the wrong product? Are there consistent delivery issues? In our example, Pete's Pivots and Pivotal Point scored the same, but is one responsible for significantly more deliveries? These are all evaluations to keep in mind when looking at product delivery.

Finally, we can look at Interoperability. This might look at how integrated CTC's systems are with each supplier. For example, is there an automated system that sends an automated message to suppliers that CTC needs to order more product if it's running below a certain threshold of pivots? How well does each company's system "talk" to other systems?

Now that we have more perspective around each attribute, which supplier would CTC prefer? The answer to this question is in the strategy for the product - a quality pivot that is a balance between affordable and reliable. In reality, this strategy may be far more complex, but in this case, it would lead us to believe that they may prefer Pivotal Point for the affordable price and high quality. That is not to discredit the lower scores for other attributes, such as interoperability or long-term potential, but rather highlight that there may be areas for improvement in the supplier relationship going forward. With more business, Pivotal Point may even become a *strategic supplier*, a concept we will discuss in the next section.

It is important to remember that the pivot is just one product. A Supplier Evaluation Matrix may be necessary for each product that you source. Looking back to our CTC scissors, if Connie's Cutting Corner is potentially interested in purchasing 400 scissors annually, and each pair of scissors requires 0.25 units of steel to produce, can the existing supplier base support an additional 100 units of steel throughout the year? Some of the questions from the Procurement Department around this decision may include the following:

a. How might that impact the supplier relationship, quality and service levels, or delivery?

b. When would the steel be delivered? Will there be adequate storage for more raw steel?

c. How far in advance do steel orders need to be placed? Is there an order cancellation period if Connie's Cutting Corner does not place an order?

d. Are there any existing or new suppliers that may be able to offer bulk discounts for ordering larger quantities of steel?

e. If Connie's Cutting Corner is requesting a 5% reduction in price, are there suppliers that could offer a lower price, with whom CTC is not currently doing business?

f. Should new and additional steel suppliers be identified and evaluated for potential business?

These are all questions to be asked for a product with an existing set of suppliers in place. But what would this mean for sourcing a completely new product? You will also recall that Customer A wants to purchase a scissors that has a grip on the handle. It was decided that this product would be brought to market. When the product was developed and tested for feasibility, it was determined that the plastic for the handles and an industrial strength glue would be needed to attach the handles to the stainless-steel blades. As a result, there was an updated BOM created, that shows the raw materials requirement for the new product.

3

Figure 3.3

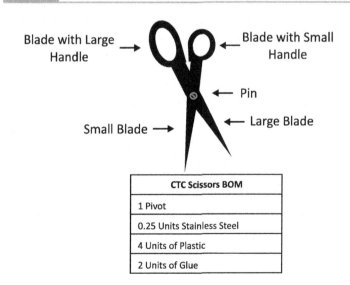

CTC Scissors BOM
1 Pivot
0.25 Units Stainless Steel
4 Units of Plastic
2 Units of Glue

This introduces complications for individuals in the Sourcing and Purchasing departments, because although demand is relatively clear – Customer A will instead purchase 400 units of the scissors with a grip, there may not be current CTC suppliers that offer the correct plastic or glue that is needed. For an annual demand of 400 units, this will require 1600 units of plastic, and 800 units of glue. What might be some considerations for the Procurement Functions as a result?

3

a. Glue and Plastic are new products for CTC, which has not traditionally been involved in these industries. What is the market landscape for each raw material, who are the key players, and what are going market prices?

b. What is the strategy for procuring each material? Should CTC consider long-term contracts with suppliers if there is uncertainty in how the product will actually perform in the market aside from just Customer A?

c. If Customer A ends up purchasing the scissors with a grip, it will require 0.10 less units of steel. What is the impact to current steel suppliers? Connie's Cutting Corner may fill in the gap of demand for steel, or even increase the amount needed from suppliers. Are there minimum order agreements already in place with suppliers? Would they be violated?

d. What is the lead time for purchasing glue and plastic? How far in advance will orders need to be placed?

e. How much inventory of plastic and glue should be ordered? When will it be delivered and where will it be stored?

f. Sadie's Scissor Shop can offer the scissors with a handle for 25% above CTC's traditional scissors price point. Will the raw material costs be too expensive to compete at this price point and still earn a reasonable margin?

You may notice that the questions around the existing product that CTC already produces differ in many respects to the questions around ordering materials for a new product. Although the launch of a new product may introduce uncertainties, the Procurement function is responsible for managing these changes and fluctuations on a regular basis. The reality is that there will never be two Sourcing scenarios that are the exact same.

3

With so many questions about which suppliers to use and how they may be impacted by CTC's decisions, it is important to define a relationship structure for the supplier base, as this may make reacting to fluctuating circumstances more manageable.

Strategic Sourcing and Partnerships

Note that for each raw material needed by CTC, there has been a group of suppliers available to provide the item. This avoids having too much reliance on a sole source of supply. Imagine that CTC only purchases Pivots from The Pivot Palace, and one day their factory burns down. With little on-hand inventory, they have no Pivots for CTC to purchase, which then may stop CTC's business and thus product delivery to customers. With multiple supplier relationships in place, CTC can reduce their overall supplier risk. How, then, can CTC decide which suppliers to allocate business to? Surely some may be more important than others.

Supplier Segmentation can help CTC evaluate which suppliers are more critical, and this determination can then drive future engagements. We can use ABC Supplier Analysis to segment CTC's supplier base for Pivots.

- "A" Suppliers are typically 10% of the total supplier base for any given product, and usually account for around 80% of business in the product category as a general rule.

- "B" Suppliers usually represent the top 25 - 30% of the total supplier base for a product, and account for around 15% of the total spend in a product category.

- "C" Suppliers are the other 60 – 65% of the total number of suppliers, and account for the remaining spend in a given category.

ABC Supplier Analysis is conducted by assessing the relative importance and spend of each individual supplier to understand how critical they are to your business. The analysis generally follows the 80/20 rule, with 80% of the impact coming from just a small 10 – 20% of the supplier base. A possible classification for CTC's pivot suppliers could be as follows:

Table 3.2

ABC Supplier Analysis - Pivots	
"A" Suppliers	Pivotal Point
"B" Suppliers	Pete's Pivots
"C" Suppliers	The Pivot Palace
	Hank's Hardware

Despite these classifications, all suppliers may be used at different times or capacities based on what the established supplier contract has outlined. These factors would include attributes such as order schedules, delivery lead times, and more.

With an understanding of how important some suppliers are over others, we can start to evaluate where it would make sense to implement **Strategic Sourcing.** Strategic Sourcing is different from a traditional procurement relationship in a number of ways.

3

Table 3.3

Traditional Sourcing	Strategic Sourcing
• Terms and Conditions Outlined for Each Order • Purchased Based Solely on Price • Little Loyalty to Supplier • Frequent Supplier Changes in Response to Market Conditions • Meet a Specific Need at a Point in Time	• Reliable Contracts in Place with Sufficient Protection • Thorough Analysis Conducted to Determine What are Cost Effective Purchases • Consistent Market Analysis • Ongoing Engagement and Problem Solving • Flow of Information with Suppliers

If CTC were to take a strategic approach to sourcing, it may allow them to better manage their business and develop closer relationships with their suppliers that align with their sourcing strategy. Although these relationships may require more resources to maintain, there are countless benefits to strategic sourcing relationships, some of which include increased flexibility, greater company alignment (both internally and with suppliers), sharing of industry best practices, cost savings, better quality, standardized pricing, and enhanced operational efficiency. Overall, closer engagement with key suppliers can ensure that CTC has a reliable supply for the raw materials that will go into production of their scissors products.

3

In this chapter, we aimed to understand the different roles and responsibilities of the Procurement function within an organization – a critical department that includes the Sourcing and Purchasing of company inputs. In doing so, we learned the following:

- *There are different materials needed to support company operations, which include direct and indirect items*

- *Supplier evaluation criteria can be used to understand which suppliers to use*

- *Segmenting suppliers can help determine how critical they are to a company's business*

- *Strategic sourcing relationships offer substantial benefits and help ensure there will be an adequate supply of inputs when needed*

With inputs being delivered to CTC, we will move on to the manufacturing   function in the next chapter to see how the plans we have put in place will perform against changing consumer preferences and variation in demand.

Chapter 4

Manufacturing

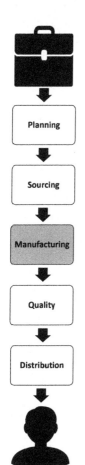

anufacturing is the step within the Supply Chain where products come to life. If customer orders cannot be filled with existing inventory, they need to be made, just as any products in inventory were made at a previous point in time. Manufacturing incorporates the raw materials, labor, equipment, tools and processing agents necessary, and turns them into outputs that generate income for a company. We saw previously how the planning and sourcing functions work together to ensure that the necessary resources are in place to make the manufacturing step possible. At the center of the Supply Chain, manufacturing makes key processing decisions based on what is provided by upstream operations, and those decisions will heavily influence the products available for the end customer.

In this chapter, we cover various aspects of manufacturing, which will include the following:

- *What manufacturing processes are and how they are designed*

- *How manufacturing constraints are introduced and the impacts they have on manufacturing processes*

- *Modern manufacturing management methods and their applications*

4

At the most basic level of all manufacturing operations, there are guiding principles that help ensure the safety and quality of the products being produced. These are referred to as **Good Manufacturing Practices (GMP)**, and include the following elements:

Safety   The manufacturing environment is safe for both workers and the products that will be produced. It is free of contamination and all hazards are appropriately mitigated.

Housekeeping   Keeping the manufacturing site clean and free from clutter is a daily habit. Every tool in the production area has a home where it is stored when not in use. The facility itself is maintained.

Sanitation and Hygiene   Procedures are in place to sanitize equipment and the manufacturing environment on a regular basis. There are sanitation procedures in place, as well as guidelines for employee hygiene.

Preventative Maintenance   Tools and equipment are taken care of, with maintenance being completed pro-actively and on an agreed schedule.

Process Definition and Guidance   Standard operating procedures are in place and easy for operators to follow, whether they are very experienced or it is their first day on the job.

Documentation   Steps in the production process are recorded for future reference and verification.

Quality   Quality programs and principles are ingrained into daily manufacturing activities to ensure product standards are met, risk is reduced, and the number of defective products produced is decreased.

Complaints and Product Recalls   If products are identified as hazardous in the market, there is a recall program in place outlining how to pull the product out of circulation, investigate the root cause of the hazard, and remedy the situation.

4

Communication   Proper communication channels are in place to escalate and mediate concerns in a timely fashion.

Training of Personnel   Employees are competent and equipped with the knowledge needed to do their job. There is a schedule in place for new employee training, as well as annual refresher courses for existing employees.

Management Commitment   Management is committed to ensuring the safety of employees in the factory, as well as the products made there. Management enables ongoing GMP implementation by providing the required resources and support.

Validation   Regular review or audit of performance

against the GMPs is completed. Plans are put in place to remedy any non-conformance to the GMPs

Good manufacturing practices will be discussed in greater depth in Chapter 6, when we review Quality Systems. These principles are critical to keep in mind for manufacturing, however, because they are often required to meet the guidelines set forth by regulators for the food and beverage, pharmaceutical, dietary supplements, cosmetics, and medical device industries. Although these industries require GMP, many others follow these as best practices. With a fundamental understanding of the rules that manufacturing sites follow, we can now look at how manufacturing processes are designed to produce products with these concepts in mind.

4

Manufacturing Processes

As we saw in previous chapters, the Sourcing teams would procure the raw materials to make products in the quantities specified by planning, and planning would determine how many units of the product to produce and when by taking into account existing inventory levels and the lead time to make a product given customer orders coming in. Manufacturing processes are a key factor in determining this lead time.

Manufacturing processes are the sequence of operations used to make a product, and are heavily determined by the attributes of the product that is being made. As we saw in the previous chapters, Research and Development would determine the materials used in the product and what attributes it may have in terms of dimensions, components, colors, functionality, and additional features. They would then work in conjunction with Manufacturing to determine how the product can be made effectively and in a cost-efficient manner.

In developing the process, Research and Development would need to determine the manufacturing methods needed to manipulate the raw materials going into the product. These methods may include forming, adding, removing, deforming, joining, consolidating, and heat-treating materials. Some common production techniques that may be used to manipulate such materials include the following:

Figure 4.1

4

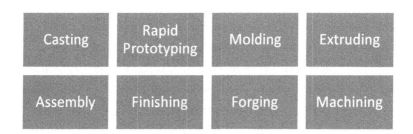

Let's look at our example of CTC, and what we are referring to as the "traditional" scissors they sell. You will recall that each pair of scissors has three components; two stainless steel metal blades each with a handle, and a pivot that holds the scissors together. We know that each scissors requires 1 Pivot and 0.25 units of Stainless Steel to produce.

Figure 4.2

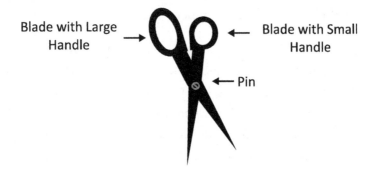

Blade with Large Handle → ← Blade with Small Handle

← Pin

4

Steel is the material of choice for the scissors because it is lightweight, yet strong enough to cut through objects without rusting. Other scissors for special purposes, such as cutting magnetic tape or explosive material, may require specialized metal alloys, but for a scissors needed for basic everyday use, stainless steel would likely be sufficient and more cost-effective than specialized materials. This would have been determined in the design stage of the product. With material inputs selected, we can look at how these materials may be manipulated to form the scissors.

You will see that the process steps we develop leverage on the attributes of the scissors. The following steps could thus be used by CTC to make the scissors:

Stamping   Given the components of steel and the pivot, we know that we want a blade with a large handle and a blade with a small handle, each of which are referred to individually as "blanks". To take the existing steel and turn it into a specific shape, it could either be melted down into molten steel and filled into a mold that is the shape of the blank and removed when cooled, or be "stamped" from a sheet of cold steel by a sharp dye that is in the shape of the blank. The handles could be welded on individually, or the blanks could be made as one piece. For our purposes, we will choose the stamping method to make the blanks in one piece, which is more often used in the industry for inexpensive scissors.

Trimming   Once stamped, the blanks are trimmed of excess metal to form their desired shape.

Drilling   With two individual blanks created, there needs to be a way to attach them to form a pair. This is where the pivot would come in, which as we learned prior is purchased from an external supplier. With each blank needing a hole in the center for attachment via the pivot, a drilling step can be included in the process.

4

Heat Treat | Cooling   The blanks are now in their desired form. Based on the properties of steel, the blanks need to be hardened to ensure their durability. The blanks can be placed in a heating chamber with the temperature raised to 1450°F for a couple of hours, then rapidly cooled for ten minutes and then cooled by ambient air for one hour. They may be rapidly cooled with air, oil, or water. This is determined based on the type of steel used and the desired characteristics of the blade.

For example, cooling at a higher temperature may make the metal softer, but yield a greater degree of toughness when it is cooled. Alternatively, heating at a lower temperature may result in more brittle material. The temperature, amount of time heated, and the substance used to cool the steel can all be manipulated within the process, and each adjustment will result in a slightly different product.

Flattening   Let's say that the warming and cooling causes the blanks to warp. As a result, they may need to be flattened again with a hammer.

Sharpening | Polishing   With the blanks in place, the blades can be formed by grinding each on a sanding belt to form a sharp edge. The edge can then be polished using a smaller sanding belt with smaller particles.

Assembling   Then, the pivot can finally be inserted to hold the blanks together, forming the scissors.

Finishing   The last step is to double check that the blades work together correctly, and if not, to adjust them. Lubricants may be used to ensure the pivot allows the handles to move easily.

After this step, the product is complete and can be sent for packaging. The various steps in the process work together to create the end product, which often is depicted by a **Process Flow Diagram**. Process Flow Diagrams are used to clearly document the process and show the relationship between different processing steps within a manufacturing plant using flow charts. Symbols and notations are used to depict the process and include major equipment, piping, direction of flows, connections with other systems, control valves, recirculation systems, process stream names and operational data such as temperature, energy, density, and pressure. At a basic level, flow charts include the following elements:

Figure 4.3

Symbol	Purpose
	Start/End
	Arrows
	Input/Output
	Process
	Decision

From the steps outlined above, we can create a simplified flow chart (note this does not include the level of detail required by the Process Flow Diagram) for the basic CTC scissors.

4

Figure 4.4

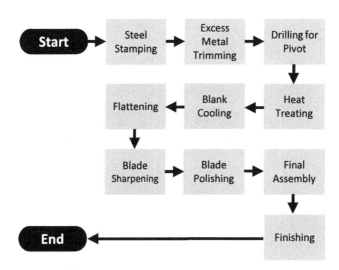

This diagram separates out the Heat Treat and Blank Cooling processes, due to the distinct nature of these tasks, as well as the fact that the amount of time required for these steps to be completed varies dramatically from the other tasks. This highlights an important point— different departments may be set up to complete various steps within the process. Thinking back to the manufacturing "line" discussed in Chapter 2 regarding planning and balancing production, we may actually see that individual production operators are doing multiple steps along this manufacturing line. A **Manufacturing Line** or production line is defined as the sequential operation within a manufacturing facility in which materials are manipulated and refined to make end products or components that will be used for further assembly. For example, we may see our straight line split into individual sub-departments as shown below, each with its own responsibilities for completing the scissors.

Figure 4.5

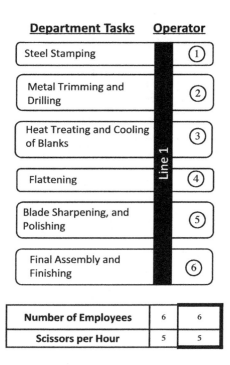

There are different ways in which tasks can be divided into individual departments. This can be determined not only by how long each step takes to complete, but also the skillset required by the operators, the equipment and tools needed, or the availability of plant resources. It is also critical in designing the process to determine the manner in which unfinished goods will flow through these departments. Products will flow differently depending on the volume required and their complexity. They will flow in one of the following ways:

Figure 4.6

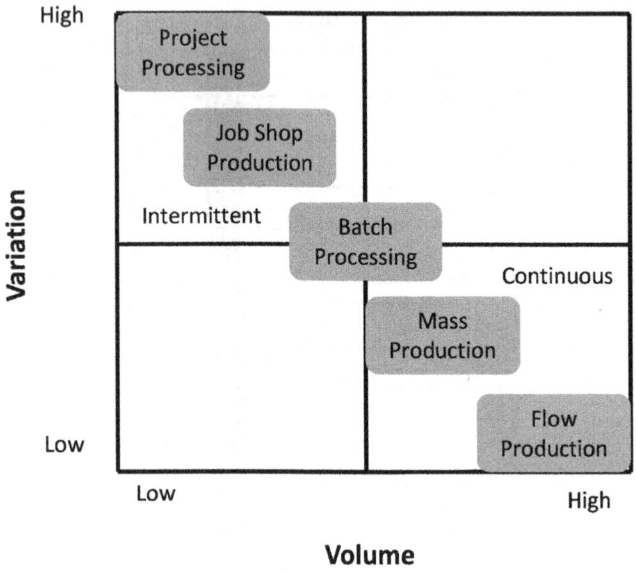

You can see that for products where there is little volume required, you may choose to make them in a Job Shop, or on an individual basis. For products that need to be made in a high quantity and on a repetitive basis, you may choose Mass Production or Flow Production where the products are consistently made by flowing seamlessly from one operation to another. For CTC, the process we defined would use Mass Production, with the exception of the Heating and Cooling steps which would use a Batch Processing flow. **Batch Processing** means that products are made in groups, not in a continuous flow. For the blanks, this would mean that after they are trimmed and drilled, they would not be put into the heating chamber directly, but rather, once 100 individual blanks accumulated, they would be put into the heating chamber together for the two-hour heating cycle.

From our CTC example, you may also wonder how five scissors per hour can be produced, when we know that it takes three hours and ten minutes (two hours heated, ten minutes rapid cool, and one hour air cooled) for the heating and cooling steps alone. This is because the heating and cooling steps may operate independently of the traditional manufacturing line. They may build inventory of the blanks above demand, or what customers have ordered, so that when the scissors are being made, the heating and cooling process does not slow down the other steps in the manufacturing line. This might mean that the blanks that are stamped and trimmed on a given day may not be flattened, sharpened, and finished until the next day's production — as in, they would build inventory of trimmed blanks to be used for future production runs.

4

Let's take a look at what this means for the timing of the traditional scissors production. We know that if five scissors are produced per hour, that means each scissor takes a total of 12 minutes. Thus, we may see the time allocated for each step in producing a scissors as follows:

Table 4.1

Process Step	Time Required
Steel Stamping	30 Seconds
Metal Trimming and Drilling	2 Minutes
Flattening	30 Seconds
Blade Sharpening and Polishing	5 Minutes
Final Assembly and Finishing	4 Minutes
Total	**12 Minutes**

Remember, we are separating out the heating and cooling procedures and assuming that these will be delivered to the manufacturing line for use by the downstream operations. If the factory is set up this way, these considerations would be taken into account at the planning phase to ensure that adequate materials and labor would be available at each step within the process to match supply and demand.

We have not yet addressed the area or department that would handle rework. **Rework occurs when** partially complete items require reprocessing or redoing of an activity somewhere along the manufacturing line because the activity was done incorrectly the first time or is not compliant with the specifications of the product. Essentially, the unfinished goods need to be fixed by either re-running them through the process, or following a different process entirely. Rework can be generated from various steps along the manufacturing line, and could include instances of excess metal not trimmed from the blanks or a loose pivot, in the case of the CTC scissors process. Rework items must be distinguished from those that are defective. **Defects** are finished items that would not meet the original intent of the product being produced. In our case, this might be a pair of blanks that do not align, inhibiting the ability for the scissors to actually cut anything. If they cannot be fixed, they would be sent to scrap as unsalable product.

Another consideration for developing the Manufacturing processes that we did not take into account for CTC would be the level of specialization required of the product. In the case of CTC, the scissors is offered in one form with no specialization. For products such as consumer electronics, aircraft, or medical devices, however, there may be various components that need to be adjusted to make the final product. Take buying a car, for example. Features such as a sunroof, heated seats, or a rearview camera all can be added to the original model. As a result, these additional features dictate the type of manufacturing used. We can see the different requirements below.

Make–To–Stock These are products with a low level of customer specificity. They are often produced in batches and held as stock until needed. These would include items such as consumer goods.

Make–To–Order Products that have high demand but have many variations are often made specifically to the orders that come in for them. These may include electronics, such as computers.

Assemble–To–Order As the opposite of Make – To – Order, if a product has infrequent demand but variations on finished products, the individual components or modules may be constructed and stored, then assembled based on the orders that come in. This would apply to the example of producing a new vehicle.

Engineer–To–Order These are products that are complex, and have unique specifications. This could include products like spacecraft or ships.

As you may note, each of these various methods are based on the specific product and industry that you may be working in or with, the customer base, and the attributes of the products themselves. If, for example, you wanted to enter a highly specialized industry, you may not be able to engineer products internally. This involves a decision to either make finished products yourself or buy them from someone else. This is known as the **Make vs. Buy Decision**. This question whether you should produce items internally or buy them from a supplier in the external market is a strategic decision. Your answer may depend on the environment the industry is facing or uncertainty about the future. It could also be dictated the existing **Capacity**, or maximum available production level, of the company. To make this decision, we would consider the following:

Table 4.2

	Make	Partner or Co-Manufacture	Buy
Control Level Required	Low	Medium	High
Advantages	Low Cost, Quality Control, Product Knowledge Internally	Knowledge Sharing, Joint Commitment	Technical Ability, Scale
Disadvantages	Capacity Constraints, Personnel Management	Partner Management	Supplier Management, High Cost

In the case of CTC, they choose to make the blanks internally and outsource the production of the pivots. This may be because the core value of their product is achieved through the quality of the cutting done by the scissors, of which the pivot plays a secondary role to the sharpness of the blade. In reality, most products would have far more components to consider in the Make vs. Buy Decision. Companies would likely sell more than one product as well, forcing them to decide which products they want to make themselves and which products they want to buy from other producers to then offer in their product portfolios.

A company can unleash a number of benefits depending on how they set up their process to align with overall company goals. Decisions around the type of materials used, technology, accuracy, quality, and division of labor all impact the capability of your process. **Process Capability** is an expression of how consistent and repeatable the manufacturing process is at meeting the product specifications, and measures the degree to which the specifications are met. Once you have an understanding of the process that is in place, you are able to predict the reliability and continued performance of your manufacturing activities.

With a fundamental understanding of how a process is created, we can look at ways in which the process can be managed to increase production efficiencies, reduce the amount of waste created, and minimize production constraints.

4

Theory of Constraints (TOC)

Production constraints are inherent in all processes; therefore, it is important to briefly touch on how they can be mitigated. **Constraints** are limitations or restrictions that inhibit the manufacturing process. These are commonly referred to as **Bottlenecks**. Bottlenecks are often seen as the point in the process that prevents it from running more quickly. In our example of the CTC scissors, the blade sharpening and polishing step took five minutes – a full minute more than the next time-consuming activity, assembly and finishing. As a result, the scissors cannot be assembled and finished until the blade step is complete; therefore, the operator doing the finishing step would finish in four minutes, and have a full minute of wait time before the next set of blanks were ready to be assembled. What this example high-lights is the Theory of Constraints.

The **Theory of Constraints** tells us that any manageable system or process is unable to achieve more than the ability of the bottlenecks within the process flow. The main premise is to exploit the constraints that exist by making them the top priority of the system and to ensure they are always operating at the best of their ability, as your entire process cannot go quicker than your bottleneck will allow. Constraints can be both internal, such as equipment abilities or company policies (i.e. no overtime), or external, such as raw material availability or a lack of consumer demand.

A unit of measure that indicates how well you are manag-ing your bottlenecks is **Takt Time**. Takt Time is the average time between the start of production of one unit and the start of production of the next, when these rates are meant to match that of consumer demand. Essentially, this tells you how quickly your production process should be running to meet the required number of units your customers are demanding. In the case of CTC, we saw that 75 scissors were demanded in March. By run-ning one 8-hour shift with 6 employees, 5 scissors are produced per hour. That means that there are 160 available hours (20 work days in a month X 8 hours per day) to produce the scissors. To calculate the Takt Time, we simply divide the available time by the number of units. As a result, we would get a Takt Time of 2.13, which means that one scissors would need to be produced about every two hours – well under the rate at which CTC is cur-rently capable to run, making the constraint a bit less concerning.

Nonetheless, for CTC, this may mean always ensuring that there is inventory of flattened blanks waiting to be turned into blades. As the bottleneck, it may already accumulate inventory at this point naturally. This eliminates additional waiting that would occur downstream, as the finishing and assembly operator would not only be waiting for an additional minute for blade sharpening and polishing, but also the extra minutes that the blade sharpening and polishing operator was waiting as well. As such, the mitigating measures that support the Theory of Constraints can be summarized in the form of a cycle.

Figure 4.7

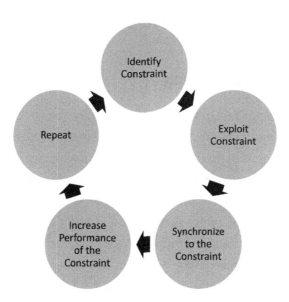

4

With an understanding of how constraints play a part in the manufacturing process, and how to mitigate them, we can move on to understand some of the modern manufacturing practices used and how they optimize production.

Manufacturing Methodologies

Manufacturing processes, once in place, are meant to run seamlessly. However, that is rarely the case. In response, companies have developed production systems to increase efficiency, reduce defects, eliminate waste, and track performance. Toyota was considered a pioneer in this field, developing many of these key principles including Just-In-Time (JIT) delivery, which we will discuss later in greater depth. The important point to remember is that various management methodologies can come together to form a system that will optimize the manufacturing operations of the organization.

4 Flexible Manufacturing

Manufacturing sites and equipment often can be costly to purchase and maintain. To offset such expenses and optimize the existing infrastructure, Flexible Manufacturing often is used to increase capacity and decrease downtime. **Flexible Manufacturing** is when the systems within the process are able to adjust, based on the type of product or the quantity of product being produced. This includes routing flexibility where an entirely new product can be made, or the order of the processing steps in which the product is made can change. There is also machine flexibility which allows multiple machines to have the capability to produce the same part, or to adapt to large-scale changes in volume, capacity, or capability. The benefits of such flexibility are as follows:

1. Increased Productivity with a Reduction in Direct Labor

2. Fewer Machines Needed

3. Less Manufacturing Floor Space Required

4. Lower Production Cost per Unit

5. Greater Machine Efficiency

6. Higher Machine Utilization

7. Increased System Reliability

8. Decreased Inventory of Spare Parts

9. Greater Agility

10. Higher Quality

11. Increased Production Rates

12. Shorter Lead Times

Many of these benefits are derived from the ability to do more with less – fewer machines are required, yet they are able to do a greater number of tasks. For our example of CTC, we acknowledged that it is rare that the company would have so many manufacturing lines with excess capacity going unused, given the decreased level of demand for the CTC scissors. In such case, they may consider contract manufacturing scissors for another company lacking the capacity to make scissors on its own. With flexible manufacturing in place, it may allow for product modifications to produce different scissors, for example by using a redesigned stamp dye for an entirely new scissors shape. This would allow the existing equipment to be utilized and generate profits, instead of sitting unused and idle.

Using flexible manufacturing does not go without its drawbacks, however, due to the associated complexity. The initial set-up of a flexible manufacturing system may be high and requires significant planning, with skilled laborers needed to understand the maintenance requirements of more complex machines as well as how to change them over. **Equipment Changeovers** are the steps required to convert a line or piece of equipment from doing one task to a different one, often to create an alternative product. These are inherent in any manufacturing process that has the flexibility to produce multiple items, and often incur a cost for the amount of time needed for an operator to retool the equipment. As such, manufacturing managers must evaluate many different factors within the production facility to decide if flexible manufacturing is a feasible and viable option for the company.

Just-In-Time (JIT)

Just-In-Time is a lean methodology that focuses on reducing waiting time within a system. It focuses on producing items only exactly when and where they are needed, and eliminates inventory that is built up in the process. This can achieve high volume production, reduce inventory holding costs, and eliminate outdated and damaged inventory.

Implementing JIT within an organization is a big undertaking. It may require deep relationships and integration with your suppliers, as minimal raw materials will be held in inventory, yet must be available for production when needed. It could also require quality improvements and adjustments to reorganize work spaces. Another consideration is in regard to the people operating within the system, as they may need new skills in order to work more flexibly across various functions. As such, it is critical to have JIT implementation driven by top management in order to build the right atmosphere of support.

With JIT in place, manufacturing will transition from a traditional Push manufacturing system, to a Pull system. A **Push** system is where deliveries from suppliers are forecasted by demand in the Master Production Schedule. In a **Pull** system, however, materials are delivered only when needed, as in "Pulled" into the process. This requires significant coordination and planning, and is therefore a critical consideration when determining how the manufacturing process will be managed.

Manufacturing Scorecard

A final tool that is helpful for manufacturing processes is a Scorecard. A **Manufacturing Scorecard** is used to track how the manufacturing operations within a company are performing. It serves as a feedback loop and identifies areas where improvement could be needed. Key metrics are identified and monitored based on the strategic goals the company is trying to accomplish. Common metrics for manufacturing performance may include the following:

4

a. Inventory Accuracy

b. Average Yield %

c. % made to Plan

d. Labor Productivity

e. Equipment Utilization

f. Downtime

g. Rework % (the amount of product that is made incorrectly that must be fixed)

h. Defect Rate

i. Scrap ($) (the amount of product made incorrectly that cannot be repurposed)

The goal is that the scorecard is balanced, covering various areas of the operations, and it may feed into a greater balanced scorecard that factors in metrics from suppliers as well as supply and demand planning and quality. The idea of the scorecard is that it will be consistent across different sites within the company, and provide key relevant information that is easy for stakeholders to readily interpret.

CTC Implications

We have covered many methodologies and elements of manufacturing, outlining the process that CTC would use in making its traditional scissors. You will recall, however, that CTC has also made some strategic decisions based on market demands.

1. A new product, a scissors with a grip, will be brought to market to meet the demands of existing and potentially new customers.

2. Connie's Cutting Corner is interested in purchasing 400 units annually. This is contingent upon a 5% discount that CTC is unsure they are able to offer.

The first scenario has significant manufacturing implications, so we can use our newfound understanding of manufacturing principles to analyze the implications of this decision. The second scenario relates more closely to Continuous Improvement, and will thus be discussed in depth in Chapter 5 regarding Quality.

If the scissors with a grip is to be brought to market, we may take into account the following considerations.

a. Will the plastic handles be purchased from an external supplier or made internally? If made internally, where in the facility will they be made? Is there space?

b. How will the plastic handles be made? It will likely r quire a plastic extrusion and forming process. What will this look like? What are the process steps required to make the handles and attach them to the blades? Employees will need proper training on how this new process can be done.

c. What equipment is required for the plastic forming process? Would that equipment serve multiple purposes? How much would the equipment cost and how fast can it produce the handles? What maintenance would be required?

4

d. How will the existing blank production need to be modified to make just the blades without the handles? How will they be attached to the plastic handles?

e. With these additional process steps, how much longer will the lead time be? Will more employees be required to achieve the same production rate of 5 scissors per hour? How does this impact process capability?

f. Does the plastic handle introduce new constraints into the process? If so, how can these be exploited?

Given the number of considerations with adding a plastic handle, you can see a relatively simple change to the scissors would require a significant commitment of resources. For this reason, it might make sense to buy the plastic handles from another company that already has the extrusion capabilities. This would allow CTC to test the viability of the scissors with the grip before committing to purchasing the equipment and taking the plastic extrusion process in-house. We must also remember that Sadie's Scissor Shop can offer the scissors with a handle for 25% above CTC's traditional scissors price point. Could CTC compete if they need to purchase equipment, train new employees, and develop new processes? We will briefly discuss product costing in the next chapter to better understand how this determination would be made. If CTC manufactures its own plastic handles, would they be able to meet the same service metrics that they were able to previously for their customers? This would require substantial analysis that falls outside the intent of our understanding, but given the number of hurdles, it is unlikely that CTC could compete efficiently enough to justify making the scissors handles themselves. If, however, this new product was viewed as a strategic decision to enter the market for these products long-term, the conversation may be different.

4

One element that we will not touch on in-depth but that we should be aware of within the Supply Chain is Packaging. Once an item finishes the. manufacturing process, it must be put in a package for the end consumer, as well as to be transported. This is often determined by a team of Packaging Engineers during the product development phase. They will determine the packaging that is suitable to protect the product from damage, yet remains functional for the target consumer. There are a number of factors to consider such as the distribution channel, product safety, quality standards, preservation requirements, fragility, and product size that all dictate the type of packaging used and the information that it contains. For something like the CTC scissors, there may be a cardboard back that provides durability for the packaging, with a clear plastic covering that allows customers to see the product while it is displayed in the aisle at a major retailer and also prevents any injury from the blades. The retailers selling the product may also have requirements of how the product is sent to them – say 20 units per box of a specified size – that make them easy to move and handle. We will discuss distribution in greater detail in the coming chapters, but for our purposes it is important to simply acknowledge the packaging step as the link between the product being manufactured and the logistics functions that follow.

Throughout this chapter we covered many different techniques, tools, and strategies that are used to make decisions for manufacturing. In doing so, we learned how manufacturing can take the ideas and feedback from the consumer market and turn those demands into reality through the products produced. This is accomplished by answering key questions about the product you are manufacturing, and the respective process that will result.

4

To summarize, in this chapter we have learned the following:

- *Best Practices used in manufacturing*

- *Key determinants for designing a manufacturing process*

- *How to identify and mitigate constraints within a process*

- *Methodologies that can be used to increase flexibility, reduce wait time, and track the effectiveness of manufacturing operations*

The manufacturing processes take significant coordination with other departments in the organization to operate effectively. Imbedded in these processes are quality principles and programs that are created to support the products being offered to customers. We will dive into these next.

This page is intentionally left blank

Chapter 5

Quality

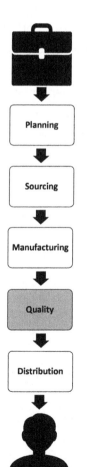

Planning

Sourcing

Manufacturing

Quality

Distribution

Quality plays a critical role in the manufacturing function, and also can be ingrained at various levels within other areas of the supply chain as well. Quality ensures that products meet internal company standards for a product which can be driven by regulatory, safety, sustainability, and customer concerns. With the right quality programs in place, the operations within an organization have standards and guidelines to steer employees toward doing their daily tasks to move the organization forward. As such, Quality serves as the last line of defense that a company has before the products and services it offers leave their four walls and are sent on for consumers to purchase.

In this chapter, we cover various aspects of manufacturing, which will include the following:

- *What are the programs required to develop a Quality Management System*

- *How quality can be viewed in terms of a process through Total Quality Management*

- *Process Improvement tools that can be used to implement and enhance quality programs within a company's operations*

Quality is highly culture driven, and needs to be supported from the top down in order to truly leverage the benefits of good quality management. At the highest level, Quality Management consists of the actions used to oversee the activities within an organization that are required to maintain a certain level of excellence. Quality Management can be further broken down into the following categories.

5

Figure 5.1

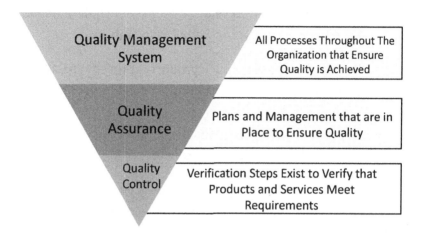

Essentially, Quality Management is the foundation upon which Quality Assurance and Quality Control can be developed. This entire system works together to embed quality standards and requirements into the organization.

Many benefits can be realized by implementing systems for Quality. Some of the most common are as follows:

Reduction in Liability   Quality programs can identify and help mitigate potential hazards before they actually happen, and develop an approach to responding to them if they occur.

Improved Safety   Not only will your products be safer for consumers, but also may be safer for your employees to produce internally with guidelines for safely executing the process.

Customer Loyalty   If customers know that they can harness the perceived value of your product, they are likely going to choose your offering in the future.

Repeat Business   If a product is proven reliable, customers may purchase multiple units to serve various purposes that they may have for them. This may also improve your market position as consumers are choosing your product over the competition.

It is also important to note that in addition to these various benefits, quality procedures may be mandated by regulatory bodies. These organizations are put in place to protect consumers by ensuring that their health and safety are maintained. They are typically public authorities or government agencies that serve in a supervisory role, and provide guidance on how certain industries should behave. Not all industries are supervised by regulatory bodies, but some of the most common in the United States, along with some of their respective regulators, are provided below:

5

Table 5.1

Industry	Regulatory Bodies
Medical Devices	U.S. Food and Drug Administration (FDA)
Cosmetics	U.S. Food and Drug Administration (FDA)
Auto and Transportation	National Highway Traffic Safety Administration (NHTSA)
Finance	Securities and Exchange Commission (SEC), Federal Reserve System
Food and Beverage	U.S. Food and Drug Administration (FDA)
Consumer Products	U.S. Consumer Product Safety Commission (CPSC)

These will vary by the level of guidance and supervision needed in the industry, with the regulatory body and policies varying by country. There are also overarching regulatory bodies that are not industry-specific. They cover guidelines across a wide spectrum including everything from pollution, nuclear safety and noise restrictions, to employee health and safety and wage protection. Accordingly, organizations are required to pay attention to the regulatory implications for their business, and put plans in place to meet any necessary standards. Such plans often fall under the realm of Quality Management.

Quality Programs

Such plans are often systematic approaches for monitoring and documenting the various tasks needed to achieve a company's standards for quality. These are often referred to as **Quality Programs**, and go beyond a simple verification check before the product is sent out to customers. To understand what programs are needed to make up the Quality Management System (QMS), companies typically follow the approach below:

5

Figure 5.2

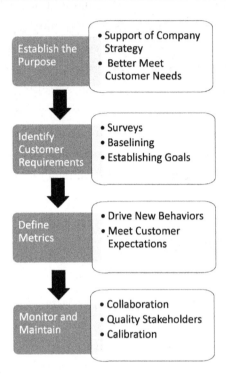

5

To put this approach into perspective, let's look at how CTC might define their Quality Program requirements. As the traditional scissors is their only product that they have sold for over 50 years, they may take great pride in their product being consistent and reliable, with a goal to not only be present in as many consumer homes as possible, but to make the CTC name one that is recognized by future generations. This idea would be incorporated into their company strategy, and would drive the need for a quality program to maintain a sufficient standard for consumers to keep the CTC name top of mind.

Next, CTC may look at what consumers want in a scissors,

which will help them make relevant products for evolving consumer demands. For a scissors, this may include the thickness that the scissors are able to cut through, or the length and shape of the blades. If length is a concern, perhaps a procedure is needed to measure the individual blades being made. With the understanding of what the customer wants, metrics then can be defined. If the desired blade length is 3.5" each, then perhaps a metric would be implemented to track the number of deviations that were over or under this length, given it is a key customer consideration. Finally, CTC would look at each individual quality precaution needed, create the individual sub-programs, and manage the larger quality system so that when issues occur, they can be mediated and resolved.

With an understanding of what quality programs are needed, let's take a look at the various forms in which they come to life.

- **Standard Operating Procedures (SOP)**   Often guidelines are created for how different tasks within the process may be carried out. These go deep into the sub-process steps, and outline quantitative measures that can be used to gauge if the step is being done correctly. For example, with the customer requirement for a blade length of 3.5", the SOP may outline which die is used in the steel stamping phase, where to get it, and how to attach it to the machine, run the equipment, and verify it is 3.5" using a measuring tape. SOPs are meant to provide a foolproof guide to how certain procedures are done so that if a new employee, or someone off the street who had never done the specific job before, looked at the instructions, they would be able toto complete the task effectively because the instructions were simple and clear.

- **In-Process Controls**   In-process controls are used to monitor the performance of the process, given the guidelines of the SOPs. This may include taking samples of each batch of product to verify the correct composition as it is being made, or monitoring if a product falls within its specification limits, as can be seen through manufacturing control data. There are various types of controls that can be used for validation, all of which are dependent on the type of product being made.

- **Material and Vendor Qualifications**   In addition to controls for the process, there may be controls for vendors and their materials as well. As we discussed in Chapter 3 on Procurement, Purchasing, and Sourcing, there may be criteria for qualifying (or onboarding) suppliers, by testing whether they can comply with company quality standards, and if their materials hold up in the process itself. Programs exist that can check and verify if such steps and material specifications are compliant. This will take place as the materials are being received, which are then tracked for validation. The results will be documented, with any incorrect product addressed with the supplier.

- **Deviation Procedures**   In the instance that a deviation from the product specification does occur, there are procedures for deciding what should be done with the product. They may outline evaluation criteria for deciding if the product can go to rework, or if it needs to be scrapped entirely. They also may outline the key stakeholders in the chain of command, and who is responsible for making such decisions. These procedures also may outline how to segregate and label the product so that it does not get mixed back in or mistaken for product that is compliant.

- **Process Reviews**   Once a process is in place, it is important to review and update it to ensure that it is relevant amid any changes that have occurred. These changes may include new equipment, a new product requirement, or additional steps for regulatory compliance. As these changes happen, processes will need to adapt accordingly. The frequency with which process reviews occur can be as often as monthly for new products or annually for processes experiencing little change. As they are reviewed, new recommendations or risks may come up that were not previously addressed, thus providing the need for another layer of defense for the organization.

- **Monitoring Oversight**   To ensure the system in place is effective, management of the quality system needs to be done on a consistent basis. This may include quality visits by quality managers that are not direct supervisors over the operations, to provide a fresh set of eyes. It also may include document reviews, data validation, and mock audits to test recall and regulatory inspection procedures. The level of oversight needed usually is determined by managers in the quality function.

- **Regulatory Oversight and Compliance Reviews**
Regulatory policies may change year over year, or morph over time. Reviews for regulatory compliance can be conducted to ensure that a company is up to speed with the most recent regulation. There may be a formal process in place for validating regulatory compliance, along with regulatory specialists in place to interpret and communicate the implications of new or changed regulations.

5

- **Audits and Inspections**   Audits and inspections are used as tools for testing how effective the existing quality programs are. These can be done internally or externally to validate the existing procedures. Formal audit criteria can be developed based on what processes are in place, while varying the non-critical components of the operation to be included. The frequency and duration can vary greatly. Once complete, the results are documented in a report, outlining corrective actions to be taken.

- **Risk Management Plans**   Risk assessments can be conducted within a manufacturing facility or through process review. As such, risk management plans can outline what the risks are within the company operations, how they can be mitigated, and what procedures to follow if they do happen.

- **Document Control**   As documents are generated within the production process, such as time logs, production data, and inspection sheets, these all need to be assigned a document number and stored in an orderly fashion that is easy to access in the future. As policies are updated, naming conventions are in place to show what is a current versusa revised version. Document Control programs typically outline when new documents are needed, how they are created, how often they should be reviewed, procedures to modify them, where to store and distribute them, and who should be given access.

- **Training**   Training of employees happens at all levels and at various times throughout an organization. Whether it be initial training for a new employee, a refresher course for an existing employee, or training on a new type of task, the training material itself needs to be updated and controlled. Often there are broader training manuals for, say, a utility factory worker, and more in-depth training programs for very technical roles. In each case, the frequency and duration of training is dependent on the position, but any level of training ensures that employees have the most up-to-date information that they need to complete their tasks in a safe manner, and ultimately deliver value to customers.

- **Quality Metrics**   Historical performance often can be understood by analyzing key metrics. As mentioned previously, metrics can tell you how you are meeting specific key consumer criteria, or where there is room for improvement. These often include specific metrics to track the effectiveness of the quality programs to convey the overall health of the quality system. Common quality metrics include customer satisfaction (which can be measured by customer feedback, complaints, or partially by product returns), defects, corrective action events, cost of quality, yield, and audit performance measures, among others.

Each of these can be developed internally, or with the help of external experts. The idea that the customer comes first is critical to keep in mind. Once developed, these programs need ongoing attention to ensure their relevancy and effectiveness for the organization. As such, the process for developing, implementing, and maintaining a quality program can be summarized as follows:

5

Figure 5.3

Plan
- Aligned Resources
- Risk Based Thinking
- Requirements Identified
- Procedures Established
- Regulatory Consideration

Do
- Nonconformance Reports
- Inspections
- Process Updates
- Performance Agreements

Check
- Customer Feedback
- Audits
- Benchmarking
- Metrics Monitoring

Act
- Full Quality System Development
- Ongoing Training and Learning
- Support Processes
- Root Cause Analysis and Continuous Improvement

5

Quality is maintained by people through diligence and careful planning; therefore, the key point to remember about quality programs is that for them to be effective, there must be buy-in from managers and key stakeholders alike. Without it, any single quality program is close to impossible to implement as it will lack the resources to keep its intended purpose alive.

Total Quality Management

With a Quality Management System in place with supporting quality programs, we can start to look at different strategies
for managing the system. Over time, one philosophy that has
gained considerable support is called Total Quality Management (TQM). **TQM** is the idea that quality should be viewed
as a process, with all aspects of the company being connected,
rather than a state that the organization is in. The way in which
it differs from product quality alone is simply the scope – being
that of an overall process instead of an individualized function.
In essence, the products manufactured should mirror the level of
quality that is embedded in the process that made it.

Let's look at the case of CTC as an example of how TQM can
be practiced. In terms of personnel, the company must hire good
workers that are skilled, say in blade sharpening or finishing,
and maintain their level of expertise through continuous learning. The environment that they work in must support stream-
lined, efficient work. For the work that they complete, they must
be paid well and on time. They must feel empowered with the
ability to ask questions and make recommendations for improvements. All of these elements come together to support the
overall quality goals of the company. This is different than simply making a high-quality scissors, as this example demonstrates
a high-quality process in and of itself.

Various factors are at play in implementing TQM. The standards that are defined for the Quality Management System are
set internally, which then form the foundation upon which other
elements interact. We can see what these elements are in the
below diagram.

5

Figure 5.4

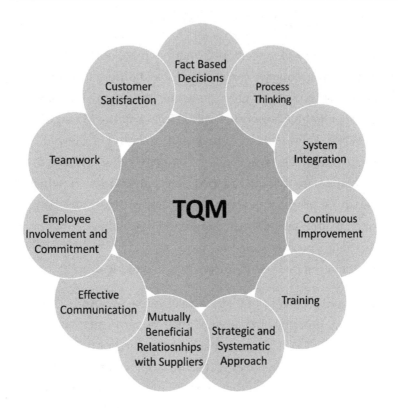

As you can see, all aspects within the company must be constantly striving to support TQM. This interaction allows for various angles of feedback to improve the process. Continuous Improvement is one area we have not touched on that is worth digging into deeper. This will help us better understand how companies not only seek improvement, but are able to put actionable steps in place.

Continuous Improvement

Organizations are tasked with improving their processes for various reasons – these can include internal factors — such as safety concerns, cost-cutting, higher quotas, or new opportunities – or can be externally driven by customer requirements or regulatory changes. **Continuous Improvement** involves identifying, analyzing, and improving the existing processes in an organization. It may also include process optimization. Although no process will ever be perfect, there are key methodologies that can be used to drive improvement efforts, to reach a higher level of effectiveness for the organization.

Lean

Lean or Lean Manufacturing combines Continuous Improvement, Quality, and Short Cycle Times to eliminate waste without jeopardizing productivity in a manufacturing process. Lean aims to highlight areas that add value, and reduce those that do not. There are various tools under the umbrella of lean, which include JIT, Takt Time, and Bottleneck Analysis which we discussed earlier in the section of the previous chapter about Manufacturing Methodologies. Other tools include standardized work, performance management, problem solving, visual management, and audits, among others. Some Lean concepts are covered by the GMPs we discussed earlier, such as standard operations and preventative maintenance.

One particularly prevalent Lean concept deals with identifying waste, and is known by the acronym TIMWOOD. Also known as the **7 Wastes**, these are sources of waste that can be introduced into a manufacturing system that once identified,

5

should be mitigated or eliminated if possible. The acronym reads as follows:

Transport   Unnecessary movement of objects

Inventory   Excess work-in-progress, parts, or materials that are not being used

Motion   Unnecessary movement of parts or people

Waiting   Time a person or product is waiting because the next step in the process is not ready for them

Overprocessing   Excess detail added to the product that does not add value

Overproduction   More products produced than what is required to meet demand

Defects   Creating the wrong products or services that can't be used

The premise of eliminating these wastes in the production system is that their elimination will reduce costs. The 7 Wastes concept also monitors which activities being completed are critical in order to bring the desired value to the customer.

5S is another Lean methodology that is used, but instead of identifying waste, it outlines ways in which a workplace is organized. This aligns closely with the GMP principle of housekeeping. The 5S's are as follows:

1. Sort

2. Straighten

3. Shine

4. Standardize

5. Sustain

Following the principles of 5S ensures cleanliness and order in the environment, which in turn reduces waste while improving safety and quality.

Overall, Lean implementation strives for continuous review of the process to identify wastes and other areas that can be improved. Over time, even small improvements can create a substantial impact. This will become clearer later in the chapter when we evaluate how CTC could use process improvement efforts.

Six Sigma

Whereas Lean is designed to eliminate waste within a process, Six Sigma is a tool used for continuous improvement of the system itself by eliminating defects. It is a data-driven approach that uses statistical analysis, where the sigma represents the population's (or products') standard deviation. The standard deviation is a measure of variation (or the defective products) in the data collected about the process.

5

A critical tool used in driving improvement in six sigma projects is the **DMAIC Improvement Cycle.** The cycle is used to solve problems by Defining, Measuring, Analyzing, Improving and Controlling hiccups within a process. We can see what each of these steps considers by understanding each function within the cycle.

> **Define**   What is the problem at hand? Who needs to be involved to solve the problem? These answers will form the project team. Often a **Project Charter** is used, which outlines the objectives of the project, the project goals,

roles and responsibilities of the team members, and who the key stakeholders are. The role of the project manager is also defined.

Measure   What is the current performance level? A baseline will need to be measured in this step to track any future progress. The necessary data will be collected. This will help to narrow the focus of the project to particular pain points or problem areas.

Analyze   What are causing these issues? The data collected will need to be analyzed in an attempt to understand the root cause of the problem. The **Root Cause** is the initiating or underlying condition from which various symptoms arise, creating a causal chain of events. This is the most basic or fundamental cause of a particular problem. To determine the root cause, often a tactic called the **5 Whys** is used. 5 Whys is an investigation technique that can be used to understand the cause and effects of problems that arise. The question "Why?" is asked in response to the previous answer, thus forming the basis for the next question. Repeating this question can often lead to the root cause of the problem.

Improve   How can the problem be fixed? Solutions are generated and evaluated to understand what is the most feasible. Oftentimes these are trialed, or piloted to determine how likely they are to fix the problem on a continued basis.

Control   Who will ensure that once the problem is fixed, the solution will be maintained? Control plans are often put in place to define who is responsible for the new process, the level of support needed, documentation requirements, how the improvement will be monitored, and how the solution will be verified in the future.

By following this approach, six sigma strives to achieve quality, stability, consistency, and accuracy. This methodology, along with Lean, can be applied across most industries. When combined with the capacity and productivity initiatives of the Theory of Constraints, Lean (driving value and efficiency) and Six Sigma (driving quality and effectiveness) create a dynamic and highly effective system for continuous improvement and overall business process management.

CTC Implications

We can use our example of CTC and the scissors they are making to understand what continuous improvement efforts might look like in reality. You will remember that Connie's Cutting Corner is interested in purchasing 400 units annually; however, this is contingent upon a 5% discount that CTC is unsure they are able to offer. This problem, offering the scissors at a discount, can be solved in a number of ways. We can use the DMAIC Improvement Cycle to evaluate, but first must understand what goes into the price of the product.

5

Let's say that the current selling price of the scissors is $12.85 per unit. This price is made up of various costs including materials, labor, and overhead. We can see these costs broken down in the table below:

Table 5.2

Cost	Description
Total Direct Labor	Cost for the Laborers such as machine operators, assembly line workers, etc. who make the product (regular hours, overtime, payroll taxes, etc.)
Total Direct Materials	Materials and supplies that are directly used during the manufacture of a product (the BOM may outline the unit quantities and standard costs associated with material going into the product; this also includes scrap materials)
Consumable Supplies	Support items that do not go into the product itself, but support the manufacturing process (gloves, safety equipment, air filters, lubricants, cleaning supplies, etc.)
Total Allocated Overhead	Indirect costs of manufacturing the finished product (indirect labor and materials, depreciation of buildings and equipment, insurance, taxes, and factory maintenance costs)

5

Added on top of these costs is the markup that the company would require to meet its financial targets. Normally, such overhead costs would be spread across different products depending on the percentage of the overall volume they take up for the company. Because there is currently only one product – the traditional CTC scissors, we can skip this calculation step because it takes up 100% of the business. These costs are then added together and divided across the average monthly units that are produced. In this case, we can use the adjusted annual demand of 900 units (per the reduction in demand of 100 units by Customer E, and pending orders from Connie's Cutting Corner), divided over 12 months, for an average of 75 units. We can assume the following costs to calculate the individual cost per unit for the CTC scissors.

Table 5.3			
	Cost	Number of Units	Per Unit Cost
Direct Labor	$168.75	75	$2.25
Direct Materials	$249.75	75	$3.33
Consumable Supplies	$102.75	75	$1.37
Total Allocated Overhead	$203.25	75	$2.71
Total	$724.50		$9.66

Note that in the real world these cost numbers would likely be in the thousands or millions; however, we will use very simplified terms for the purpose of our example.

We can see from the above table that our total costs per unit are $9.66, composed of the following:

- Direct Labor = $2.25

- Direct Materials = $3.33

- Consumable Supplies = $1.37

- Total Allocated Overhead = $2.71

This means that the scissors would need to be sold for at least $9.66 in order to break even. From here, we can calculate what the Markup is by subtracting the cost price of the item from the selling price, and dividing the resulting amount by the cost. We can then multiply by 100 to get the Markup percentage for each individual unit. This is represented by the following equation:

Markup = ((Selling Price − Cost Price)/ Cost Price) X 100
CTC Markup = $12.85 - $9.66 = $3.19
3.19/9.66 = 0.33023

$$0.33023 \ X \ 100 = 33\%$$

So, this tells us that the scissors is being sold at a 33% Markup from the cost of producing the scissors. As mentioned previously, this Markup would be set to support the desired financial targets of the company. One such measure is Gross Profit Margin %, which tells you the revenue dollars remaining for the company after deducting the costs relating to the goods it sells. It is represented by the following equation:

Gross Profit Margin % = ((Revenue – Cost of Goods Sold)/ (Cost of Goods Sold)) X 100

In this equation, Revenue is represented by the number of units sold, times their selling price. Cost of Goods Sold, on the other hand, (or COGS as they are commonly referred to) are calculated by adding together your beginning inventory and purchases made during the period, minus your ending inventory for the period.

5   This is a very elementary approach for calculating the pur chase price and corresponding Gross Margin %, as we have not discussed the various accounting methods that can be used, or the calculations used for gauging overall operating profitability. For our purposes, it is important to simply remember that the company would set the Markup at 33% so that once the scissors were sold, there would be enough money to not only to break even from the costs of production and sales of product, but also keep the company running at a profitable rate.

With an understanding of where the purchase price comes from, we can now use the DMAIC approach to see if there are ways in which this can be reduced by 5% to meet Connie's Cutting Corner's request.

DEFINE	MEASURE	ANALYZE	IMPROVE	CONTROL

What is the problem? - Connie's Cutting Corner has requested a 5% reduction in purchase price.

Who should be involved to solve the problem? – As this is a cost-cutting exercise, Planning, Sourcing, Manufacturing, Quality, and Logistics will be the key sources for cost reduction efforts, with Finance in an advisory role. If there is potential for labor adjustments, Human Resources may be involved as well. There will be representation from each department on the team who will help to identify the key stakeholders in the organization.

What is the Objective or Project Goal? – Reduce sale price by 5% to $12.21 per unit from $12.85.

DEFINE	MEASURE	ANALYZE	IMPROVE	CONTROL

5

What is the current performance level? – The price is currently set at $12.85 per unit. Our baseline was developed in defining our costs ($9.66 per unit) for the product, and corresponding Markup (33%).

To reduce the purchase price of an individual unit, the company may reduce the margin they are making on the product as a quick solution. The decision would be made by the Finance and Sales department. In this case, the Markup % could be up to only 26% using our same calculation as before.

$$\text{CTC Markup} = \$12.21 - \$9.66 = \$2.55$$
$$2.55/9.66 = 0.2640$$
$$0.2640 \times 100 = 26\%$$

If Connie's Cutting Corner is seen as a long-term strategic customer, there may be justification to take a hit on the margin amount in the short run to win some of their business, given that CTC will still be exceeding their break-even point. It is also possible that because of dropping demand for the scissors, they would be willing to make less money on the scissors in order to stabilize production and incoming revenue. The company will obviously make more money, however, if the margin reduction can be avoided, so we will rule out this option for now, and use it only as a last resort.

What data will be collected? – Given the existing costs for the product, we can form an additional baseline by breaking down the categories that are the source of the greatest spend.

5

Table 5.4

	Per Unit Cost	*% of Total Cost*
Direct Labor	*$2.25*	*23%*
Direct Materials	*$3.33*	*34%*
Consumable Supplies	*$1.37*	*14%*
Total Allocated Overhead	*$2.71*	*28%*
Total	*$9.66*	*100%*

From this table, we can see that the biggest sources of spend are Direct Materials and Overhead, followed by Direct Labor. We can break down each category even further to understand what is driving these costs.

Table 5.5

Direct Materials	Cost	% of Cost	Functional Areas
Steel	$189.90	76%	Procurement & Sourcing
Pivots	$59.85	24%	
Total	**$249.75**		

Table 5.6

Total Allocated Overhead	Cost	% of Cost	Functional Areas
Indirect Labor	$56.91	28%	
Indirect Materials	$50.81	25%	Planning, Human Resources, Procurement & Sourcing, Finance/ Accounting, Manufacturing
Depreciation	$34.96	17%	
Insurance	$16.26	8%	
Taxes	$14.23	7%	
Factory Building Maintenance	$30.08	15%	
Total	**$203.25**		

Table 5.7

Direct Labor	Cost	% of Total Cost	Functional Areas
Regular Hours	$134.27	80%	Human Resources, Manufacturing, Planning
Overtime	$5.20	3%	
Payroll Taxes	$29.28	17%	
Total	**$168.75**		

What are the existing pain points? – From this data collected, we can see where the biggest costs are coming from across all sources, to identify the biggest overall product costs.

Figure 5.5

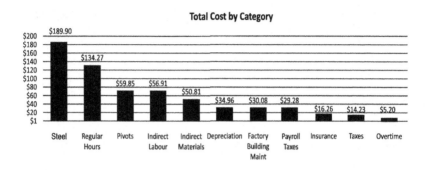

DEFINE   MEASURE   ANALYZE   IMPROVE   CONTROL

5

What is causing these issues? - It is no surprise that the greatest costs are coming from raw materials, as there are only two going into the product itself. This makes them more concentrated costs, as opposed to a more complicated product that would have raw material costs spread over various materials and components. Let's say you start asking around about your existing supply contracts for steel, and you learn that CTC's volume of steel purchased from its primary supplier is not high enough to get an 8% bulk discount on steel. CTC currently purchases 170 units of steel to support the annual demand for scissors, each of which requires 0.25 units of steel. To get the bulk discount, 200 would need to be purchased. You also learn that you could save money on steel by reducing the amount of scrap generated in the process, which currently exceeds the industry standard by a small margin.

Regular Labor hours are also a high source of spend. You will recall from Chapter 2 on planning that we identified the challenges associated with staffing 5 manufacturing lines with 30 people where it would take 3.2 hours to produce the 80 scissors needed in the month of March. Alternatively, by running one line, it would require a staff of 6 two 8 hour shifts to produce the same 80 scissors for a total of 16 hours. This may require cross training of staff so that they can work across various job assignments in the manufacturing line. You might also learn that machines could be purchased that would reduce the need for the Metal Trimming and Drilling, as well as Flattening steps within the process. We can keep these thoughts in mind to analyze potential Labor hour reduction efforts.

We will use the 80-20 rule to look further at Steel for Raw Materials and Regular Labor Hours, which are both critical to business operations but could potentially be made less costly. This is not to say there aren't opportunities in the other categories of spend that should be investigated, but rather that they may offer less opportunity.

5

| DEFINE | MEASURE | ANALYZE | IMPROVE | CONTROL |

How can the problem be fixed? - Let's say from our analysis and alignment with the broader team (remember there are stakeholders that will impact whether your initiatives will be supported), you are able to develop the table below. This allows us to see that various solutions exist to solve each problem, with the likelihood and cost for implementation, as well as the corresponding cost savings:

Table 5.8

Category	Reduction Effort	Feasibility	Overall Implementation Cost	Potential Cost Savings Per Unit
Reduce Steel Costs	Increase Purchase Quantity	Low	$8.25	$0.05
	Negotiate Supplier Agreements	Medium	$2.76	$0.60
	Reduce Material Variance (Scrap)	Medium	$0.35	$0.04
Reduce Labor Costs	Automation (Employee Reduction)	Low	$15.05	$0.58
	Reduce to One Line (Employee Reduction)	Medium	$8.40	$0.17
	Cross Train Employees	High	$2.20	$0.35
	Develop Labor Standards	High	$1.25	$0.08

Again, this does not include the potential cost savings opportunities that could come from lower cost spend categories, which could still be investigated for further cost savings. Remember that total costs for the company are $724.50 per month. The implementation costs identified for these two cost categories are relatively reasonable in light of long-term savings. It may seem like the company is spending money to save money; however, the "Potential Cost Savings per Unit" shown in the table is the annual per unit savings net of the investment price.

In terms of steel, it is unlikely that you would purchase more if you don't have existing demand for it, as you would have to pay to store it, and the corresponding savings are quite low. Alternatively, negotiating your supplier agreements, or reducing the amount of scrap that results from the production process, would cost much less to implement, for proportionately higher savings.

On the labor side, you may be able to achieve higher cost savings by introducing automation, but equipment may be costly and take time to implement. This would also incur significant legal fees to lay off employees that are no longer needed and provide them with adequate compensation packages. The same dilemma comes up for reducing the manufacturing force to one line. It may be easy to do in theory, but would have the same personnel challenges. Instead, by improving the existing labor force through cross training and the development of labor standards, you could achieve cost savings at a lower investment price in the long run.

You may notice that no individual solution will achieve the desired savings of $0.65 per unit. It is also important to note that what is listed in the table is the savings *potential* that CTC hopes to realize. In reality, company may be able to achieve only a fraction of that amount. As a result, CTC may choose to negotiate their supplier contracts (which would fall solely under the Sourcing & Procurement function) *and* cross train employees to reach the target cost savings.

To cross-train employees, a learning and development plan may be created across the Manufacturing and Human Resources functions. Planning will also be involved to schedule extra employees during operating hours to be trained. Savings will then be realized because hiring can be done internally (reducing onboarding costs), gaps in skill for doing specific operations will be avoided (and thus overtime costs for skilled employees will be eliminated), and employee retention will be improved.

DEFINE	MEASURE	ANALYZE	IMPROVE	CONTROL

Who will ensure that the solution is maintained? – There will be a shared responsibility across Planning, Manufacturing, and HR to not only implement the training schedule, but ensure that new employees are gradually brought through the cross-training process. This will require review processes as well as a training log to track the training that specific employees have completed.

A simplified control plan for CTC may look like the below table:

5

Table 5.9

Task	Owner	Responsibility	Document	Completion	Verify
Training Program and Standards	Human Resources	Learning and Development Team			
Update Requirement in Training Log	Human Resources	Factory HR Manager			
New Training Scheduling Process	Planning	Planning Manager			
New Schedule Incorporating Cross-Train	Planning	Labor Resource Planner			
Trainer Assessments to Verify Teaching Skills	Manufacturing	Manufacturing Manager			
Employee Capability Assessments	Manufacturing				
Cross Training Approval Form	Manufacturing				

5

Note that dependencies are built in, so that the deadlines for one task are based on ample time to complete the previous task required. We can see for example that the Manufacturing Supervisors create an Approval Form to sign off on employees who have completed all of the necessary cross training activities only *after* the Learning and Development team has put standards in place to define what must be done to satisfy each training activity.

Through this example of Continuous Improvement, we have

seen how CTC could indeed meet the cost reduction target of 5% in the purchase price of the traditional scissors for Connie's Cutting Corner. The timing at which these savings could be realized is a different story, and sales must be closely involved to understand when is the right time to pass along the cost savings to CTC's customers. Various entities within the Supply Chain, in conjunction with other departments across the organization, were able to come together to meet the changing expectations of customers in the market, or in this case, bring in a new customer.

Throughout this chapter we covered the various processes, programs, and management tools used by individuals who work in Quality functions. We have seen how quality can play a key role in helping a company achieve their desired level of excellence through checks and balances that ensure poor quality products do not reach their customer base. This level of diligence can thus also support new demands made by customers in the market for the products they desire.

5

To summarize, in this chapter we have learned the following:

• *How regulatory bodies influence the quality programs that are needed*

• *Which individual programs come together to form a Quality Management System*

• *The importance of embedding a culture of Quality into an organization*

• *How Quality can be viewed as a Process using TQM*

• *Which frameworks and methodologies can be used to undertake process improvement efforts, such as cutting costs*

Once products are made, such as our CTC scissors, and pass their respective quality checks, they need somewhere to go or they will build up on the manufacturing floor. This is where the logistics functions come into play to deliver the product to customers. We will discuss this function in the next chapter.

5

This page is intentionally left blank

Chapter 6

Logistics

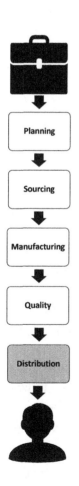

A s the last function we will discuss within the Supply Chain, Logistics represents the steps taken to not only deliver physical goods to customers, but also the respective intermediary materials. When items are purchased from suppliers, the suppliers are typically responsible for delivering them to the company purchasing them, but that is not a concrete rule. Depending on the material, the purchasing companies may take on this responsibility as well, although it is less common. Once the items are delivered, they may need to be moved around to different facilities for storage or consumption. If products have sub-components that are made at different facilities, these also may need to be moved to other sites, or can be sold on to customers. This movement of goods is the basis for the Logistics function, and ensures that finished goods can reach consumers for purchase, whether it be through a retailer, distributor, or direct customer selling approach.

We will cover the various aspects of the Logistics function in this chapter, and will learn the following:

- *How regulatory bodies influence the quality programs that are needed*

- *Which individual programs come together to form a Quality Management System*

- *The importance of embedding a culture of Quality into an organization*

- *How Quality can be viewed as a Process using TQM*

- *Which frameworks and methodologies can be used to undertake process improvement efforts, such as cutting costs*

Before we dive deeper into the specific areas that make up Logistics, we must reiterate the different types of Logistics that exist. These include the following:

- **Inbound Logistics**   These are the external upstream materials that enter into the supply chain. Inbound logistics involves the movement of such materials from their point of origin to where they need to be in production.

- **Outbound Logistics**   This involves the movement of finished goods from where they are produced to where they will actually be consumed, which we have referred to throughout this book. It is associated with the delivery of physical goods, whereas computing services or software for example, would require a form of digital delivery. Outbound Logistics are a downstream activity in response to actions of previous steps taken within the Supply Chain.

- **Reverse Logistics**   When products are unsold, damaged in the market, or expire, they must be returned to their point of origin, or production point, to be disposed of. In the case of expiration, perishable products often can be thrown away, but for more sensitive items, such as pharmaceuticals, medical devices, and chemicals, these need to be disposed of in a more diligent and responsible manner. As such, product needs to be returned to the company producing it where the company will decide how to reuse, repair, or recycle unsellable product accordingly.

We can more clearly see how the various elements of Logistics work together to support the Supply Chain in the following graphic:

Figure 6.1

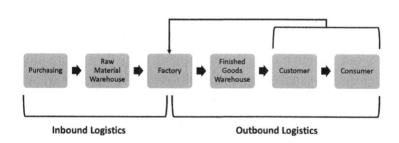

Inbound Logistics   Outbound Logistics

6

It is important to note that in this case the "Customer" could be a number of parties including a wholesaler or distributor that would sell to various retailers, or the retailer itself, such as

Walmart. We will discuss the different elements of Distribution later in this chapter.

If a company does not want to manage such Logistics functions on its own, it can outsource these functions by using a Third-Party Logistics (3PL) company. A **3PL** is a company specializing in one or all elements of the Logistics function. For example, a 3PL may specialize in fulfillment or inventory optimization tasks. Other 3PLs may provide a wide range of services, handling all elements of Transportation or Warehousing for the company. The benefits of such a relationship include more time to focus on core business activities, less overhead, and additional expertise, especially when a company is expanding internationally. Using a 3PL comes with its challenges as well. These may include high set-up fees, less control, and time required to manage the 3PL relationship. These costs and benefits must be weighed against one another to determine if outsourcing the logistics function makes sense for the company. If it does, then it will be critical to choose the right provider, and sync any existing inventory management, order management, order processing, and warehouse management systems with the 3PL to ensure seamless business operations.

6

Overall, we can conclude that Logistics is the flow of products and information that, as a result, delivers some form of financial reward or value back to the company. The areas that make up the Logistics function include Warehousing, Distribution, and Transportation, which we will dig into further to understand how such value is delivered.

Warehouse Management

Warehouses are the first Logistics step that finished products encounter coming off the production line and, therefore, play a key role in managing and storing raw materials and finished goods inventory. They serve as a place to hold products until they are ready for consumption and are typically able to store a wide range of materials. Warehouses come in various shapes and sizes, with a wide range of capabilities as well. Some of the typical types of warehouses include the following:

- **Private Warehouse** These are owned by a single manufacturer and are often at the same location as the production site. The company is responsible for the warehouse operations, quality, management, inventory tracking, and upkeep of the facility itself.

- **Public Warehouse** Spaced is leased in a warehouse that is shared by multiple companies and their respective products. The warehouse operator may provide short or long-term storage options that can be leased on a month-to-month basis. Fees are typically based on inbound and outbound transaction costs as well as storage fees themselves, which are typically calculated on a per pallet or per foot basis.

6

- **Contract Warehouse** This too is a communal warehouse; however, many of the shipping, receiving, and management tasks are handled by the warehouse staff. Whereas a Public Warehouse may be on a temporary basis, contract warehouses typically require a long-term commitment that provides for warehousing services over a longer period of time.

The type of warehouse used is heavily dependent of the requirements of your product. If say, you are a food manufacturer, you may be concerned about storing your products in a public warehouse due to the contamination potential from other products. As a result, you may choose a warehouse that is food grade, that only stores food products in a segregated area. You also may want to segregate your product from others that contain allergens, such as peanuts or shellfish. If the food product needs to be refrigerated, you would also need to evaluate which warehouses have refrigeration rooms with the ability to hold the room at a constant, colder temperature. You can start to see how your product and business strategy can help you choose the best warehousing option.

When deciding upon a warehousing solution, there are a number of considerations. Below is a list of factors to consider in addition to the product nature.

Customer Delivery Time   This will dictate the size, location, and number of warehouses needed.

Carrier Proximity   It is critical that the desired Transportation modes are able to reach the warehouse itself.

Workforce Availability   Warehouses often can be located in remote or industrial areas due to their need for expansive physical space. It is important that there is a sufficient labor force to support such operations.

Long-Term Growth   If a company hopes to grow, their warehousing selection and strategy will need to align to ensure that the warehouse space can keep up with expansion activities, such as new distribution networks or a greater number of SKUs.

With the ability to choose the appropriate warehousing solution for a company, we can now look at the management activities and responsibilities of the warehouse itself. Many warehouses utilize a **Warehouse Management System (WMS)** to support day-to-day tasks. A WMS is a software program that can help to optimize the functionality of the warehouse, while assisting with inventory management and fulfillment requirements. It may monitor where a specific product is at a given time and how long it has been there, any new inventory that was received, and inventory transfers that are required. It can also generate pick plans to show which product needs to be retrieved from the warehouse to ship out. This would apply in the case of finished product, but also can occur for products in raw material warehouses, that need to be pulled out for use in production. In conjunction, the WMS also may create critical reports for the business, such as weekly stock reports that document inventory levels, turns, and holding costs. These are highly effective because, in general, a company's WMS can manage various warehouses within the broader network of operations. It is also possible in more sophisticated operations for retailers or distributors to make orders directly from an integrated WMS that they have with the company for their inventory fulfillment.

The use of a WMS may become clearer as we look at the tasks **6** completed within the warehouse itself. The activities that the warehouse is responsible for are outlined in the chart below:

Figure 6.2

Receiving	• Delivery arrives and is unloaded on the warehouse dock • Inspection to verify delivery quantity and quality of the items
Put Away	• Product is put away in a specific location or rack • Storage location and inventory level documented in the WMS • Any adjustments are made in the WMS for physical vs. recorded inventory
Allocation	• Product is assigned to fulfill a specific order, whether individual or as replenishment • Timeframe for shipment is entered into the WMS in accordance with shipping service levels
Picking	• Pick Plan is created for operators by the WMS • Product is retrieved from its location within the warehouse • It is staged at the shipping dock to be loaded
Loading	• Individual units are taken from the dock and loaded for shipment based on sequencing • Items are inspected to ensure the correct quantity and product are being shipped • Bill of Lading (BOL) is generated that documents which is included in the shipment
Shipping	• Items physically leave the warehouse • Change in inventory levels is recorded with outgoing product in the WMS • Any damaged inventory is recorded

6

This diagram assumes that products are already in their desired configuration for shipping, which may not always be the case. Take a shipment going to a large retailer from a distributor's warehouse, for example. It may require a pallet to have multiple types of product in one group for the desired shipment. In this instance, a pallet of each individual product would need to be pulled off the shelves and unwrapped to take the desired number of boxes for the shipment. The pallet would then be rewrapped if needed, and put back on the shelf with the change in inventory recorded. This would happen for each individual product that would go on the pallet. This may seem inefficient; however, a WMS can help to minimize the number of picking activities needed, and identify the most efficient way to build the new pallet, making these systems critical to any warehousing operation.

The above diagram also illustrates the most basic example of how a warehouse may operate. In more advanced cases, they may use barcodes to assign and track inventory using barcode scanners, or they may even use RFID technology to detect where a product is or when it has passed a certain point within the four walls of the warehouse. It is also possible to utilize more complex unloading and loading strategies such as cross-docking. **Cross-Docking** is a practice used to unload incoming materials on a warehouse dock, only to load them directly into an outbound truck, trailer, or rail car with perhaps a different mix of products or in different quantities. This eliminates the need for any storage in between and can reduce delivery times and cost (with a smaller warehouse space needed and easier inventory management), while increasing customer satisfaction and, in certain cases, even increasing market share due to the ability to reach customers more quickly than competitors. Whether choosing to use Cross-Docking or advanced technology within the warehouse like RFID, each warehouse operation is unique and can add great value when aligned appropriately with the company's strategy.

6

At this point it is also important to note that the type of warehousing we have discussed thus far is primarily in relation to physical products. A barrel of oil, for example may have far different storage requirements and handling than a pallet containing boxes of consumer goods. The management of such inventory would thus be different as well, bringing us back to the key point that choosing a warehousing solution is heavily dependent on the nature of your product, in addition to the desired distribution strategy.

Distribution

Once a company's product leaves the warehousing network, it is time for it to reach its targeted consumer. Who these consumers are, and where they are located, heavily dictate the distribution strategy of the company and how the product reaches them. Let's look at a few of the common distribution strategies that are used today.

Figure 6.3

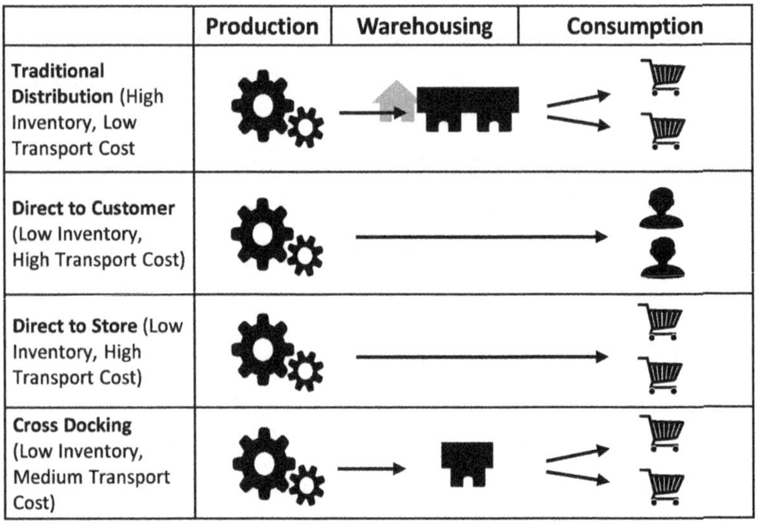

	Production	Warehousing	Consumption
Traditional Distribution (High Inventory, Low Transport Cost)			
Direct to Customer (Low Inventory, High Transport Cost)			
Direct to Store (Low Inventory, High Transport Cost)			
Cross Docking (Low Inventory, Medium Transport Cost)			

These are strategies traditionally used in the retail space. As a rule of thumb, the fewer number of "touches" on the product, typically the lower the cost associated with distributing it. There are also many implications associated with how you want customers to access your product. Do you want them to be able to purchase it directly, say from a catalog where the product can be shipped to them, or do you want your product to be accessible through a physical store? The emergence of e-commerce has dramatically changed the way in which consumers shop, as they do not have to leave the comfort of their home to purchase a product, and in addition, they may have a wider selection of products available to them than they would if they went to one individual store in person. As a result, companies need to match their distribution strategy to meet this change in demand.

To craft a distribution strategy and decide which distribution approach to use, we can ask the following questions:

1. **What business are we in?** – Who are the customers in our industry – individuals, or other businesses? Where do these consumers go for the purchase of our product? What industry trends or external events could impact their purchasing behavior?

2. **What decisions have we made about the product and the market?** – What are our customers' needs and how does the product meet them? How do the products deliver value to customers? Where are these individuals located?

3. **What customer service levels are we targeting?** – How do we meet consumers' expectations? What is their demand for our product, and how do we ensure it is available in the right place at the right time, and at the right price point?

6

Answering these key questions will help determine the avenues used to distribute the product. These must align with both the overall business strategy as well as marketing strategy to ensure your distribution channels reach your target customers. In addition, they may dictate whether to work through a Wholesaler or a Distributor. A **Wholesaler** is someone who buys a wide array of goods in bulk quantities and resells them in smaller amounts to brick-and-mortar or e-commerce retailers. Take a Mom-and-Pop convenience shop for example. They may not be willing or able to buy a full pallet of one type of candy bar that they sell, but would be willing to buy a smaller quantity, say five boxes, that they would be able to store and absorb in their inventory. A **Distributor** on the other hand, is the source of the Wholesaler's supply, reselling products they purchased directly from the manufacturer. Distributors often have exclusive agreements with the manufacturing company that allow them sole selling rights in a particular territory or region. Because they buy large quantities of one specific product, Distributors can often give Wholesalers discounts based on their purchase volumes.

Once the warehouse locations, intermediaries, and points of customer contact are defined, these are further integrated with other decisions made in the supply chain. One such instance is in regard to planning. One subset of the planning functions discussed in Chapter 2 is Distribution Resource Planning (DRP). DRP involves the ways in which distribution will be executed given the defined channels. It may build in inventory control parameters, such as we saw with the safety stock levels that CTC stipulated, and calculate what inventory is needed to meet demand in terms of physical distribution. The idea behind DRP is to minimize costs (such as those associated with ordering, moving, and storing goods), while minimizing shortages in the process as well. This is just one instance of how the distribution

6

decisions will influence and impact the broader supply chain.

Let's think back to CTC's distribution model. You may remember that the company services four regions (North, East, South, and West) out of their central warehouse that is on the same site as their factory that produces the scissors. Across all of these regions they have only three major competitors. Their demand by region is listed below:

Table 6.1

Region	North	East	South	West	
Customer	A	B	C	D	E
Demand (units)	400	96	240	114	150

The model that CTC is using is commonly referred to as the **Hub and Spoke Model,** where a centralized warehouse services various regions, thus minimizing the number of routes needed to and from various warehouse locations. In a traditional model, multiple warehouses might service multiple customers, resulting in product shuffled across warehouses or different manufacturing locations might even exist to get product where it needs to be. In contrast, the Hub and Spoke Model may have a regional hub dedicated for each customer geography that it services, such as a hub in the West region that would service Customers D and E. The airline industry is a great example of this model, given that airlines typically have regional "Hubs" (being a specific airport) with various routes connecting through them to other destinations within the region.

6

In the case of CTC, their primary warehouse is used as their distribution hub to send product out to customers, making for a relatively centralized and simplified distribution process. With this approach, they can gain efficiency and achieve economies of scale. This is a critical consideration given that Customer E is not able to sustain their demand of 150 units per year, and will be reducing their product order to only 50. As a result, CTC will be able to pivot this volume to another customer, making the transportation of goods less frequent to the Eastern region and perhaps more frequent in a different region, although not necessarily at the same rate. We must note, however, that because they are selling their products to their end "customer" (i.e. a wholesaler or retailer that will then sell the product onward) without a warehouse intermediary, they are using the Hub and Spoke Model by default. In cases where a company would be responsible for the last-mile delivery (which is delivery to the final delivery destination, most commonly the consumer at a personal residence), it may face a more complex distribution network, thus needing to further leverage the Hub and Spoke Model to minimize transportation costs.

6 Transportation

Transportation is the final area of Logistics that we will discuss in this chapter, which is typically what comes to people's minds when they think of Supply Chain, because of the visibility of the Transportation function. At a very basic level, Transportation involves the physical movement of objects from one location to another. The way in which that movement occurs can vary greatly depending on what you are moving its destination.

The movement of freight between two distant cities, using any Transportation mode, is commonly referred to as a **Line Haul**. Some of the modes of Transportation that can be used to support such movement include the following:

- Land Transport (via Rail or Truck)

- Water Transport (via Ship)

- Air Transport (via Airplane)

- Pipeline Transport

You may see that different Transportation modes are more conducive to some items than others. Take Pipeline Transport for example. To use this mode, you must be moving a liquid substance such as oil in a place where a pipeline is already constructed. In contrast, transporting oil by Air would be very ineffective from a cost standpoint due to the quantity and weight being moved, which can easily be handled by a pipeline for a much lower cost. We can see the advantages and disadvantages of each mode in the table below:

6

Table 6.2

Transportation Mode	Advantages	Disadvantages
Rail	Large Capacity, Dependable	Low Cost Savings, Higher Potential for Damage
Truck	Transit Time Efficiency	Inefficient Fuel Consumption, Safety
Ship	Efficient Fuel Consumption, Cost Savings	Long Transit times
Airplane	Quick Transit Times, Safety Large Volumes, Low Cost, Energy Efficient	High Cost, Lower Volumes Limited to Specific Products, Availability
Pipeline	Large Volumes, Low Cost, Energy Efficient	Limited to Specific Products, Availability

Depending on what is the most important factor for the goods you are moving, you may choose one mode over another quite easily. For example, if you had concerns over the capacity of your transportation vehicle, you could consider that one barge can transport the equivalent of 15 rail cars, which equates to 58 truckloads. This information would make it easier to conduct a cost-benefit analysis to see what was the most cost-effective way to move a large quantity of goods from point A to point B.

It is also possible, however, to use **Intermodal Transport,** which combines multiple transportation methods. This is commonly seen when moving goods internationally, which requires Air or Water Transport across many continents, but then also a secondary form of transport to move the goods inland to where their customers might be based. As an added benefit, Intermodal Transport can take advantage of the economies of scale that are inherent in each mode of Transportation, resulting in a lower

6

cost for the integrated service.

To understand which transportation mode to use, we must evaluate a number of factors, some of which are shown in the diagram below.

Figure 6.4

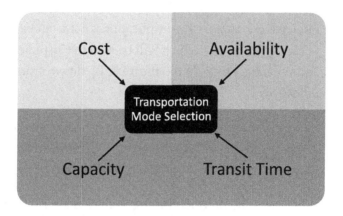

Each of these considerations must be evaluated in the context of the geography, environmental impact, and the technological needs of the company moving products. Once a company develops a transportation strategy around how they are moving their goods, it is rare that they would deviate from it unless there are unforeseen circumstances. Take a rush shipment for example. What typically may come by ship in up to 40 days, could instead be diverted to come by air in just 10 days in order to meet a production deadline. Of course, the late notice and higher shipping rate would incur additional cost, but this still may be less costly than any penalties a company may have to pay for a late shipment to their customers because the products they are providing

6

are not yet made. This small trade-off ensures that service levels are met, raw materials are where they need to be, and, ultimately, that products are reaching their end targets.

CTC Implications

Given the different responsibilities that make up the Logistics function, let's think about how this would impact CTC, given their recent decisions.

a. First, we can analyze the implications of introducing the scissors with a grip, which will be sold to Customer A and potential others in the future. CTC may consider the following:

b. How will the additional inbound logistics be handled for any new materials? Will the supplier take on this responsibility? When and how will the new materials be delivered?

c. Where will the products be stored once made? Is there enough storage capacity given the existing warehouse space? If not, what other warehouse options would be considered (buying, renting, etc.)? How should growth be accounted for?

d. How will the new scissors be integrated into the WMS? Are stock levels and inventory turn metrics defined? What reports will provide performance information?

e. Where is Customer A located? Will the same distribution network and transportation strategy be used to deliver the new kind of scissors?

f. Do the additional product attributes change the way in which the product is packaged? Are boxes of the new scis-

6

sors heavier, or a different shape, thus impacting how they sit on a pallet or are stored?

g. What are the service level metrics for delivery of the new product? Will these remain the same as for the traditional scissors they were previously purchasing?

Because Customer A was already purchasing the traditional scissors from CTC, the disruption in delivery of the product is limited, as many elements of the business relationship are already defined and established. This is slightly different when there is a new customer entering the existing mix, as is the case with Connie's Cutting Corner. In such instance, CTC may consider the following:

a. Where is Connie's Cutting Corner located? How will additional shipments reach their region? Will this impact other customers within the distribution network?

b. How far away is their store? What mode of Transportation best suits the product delivery and will be cost efficient?

c. Is product delivered to the store directly, or to a warehouse? How do they want to store the inventory, and how much inventory will they hold at a given time?

d. Is there an existing transportation provider that CTC already uses that can service the Connie's Cutting Corner route?

e. How frequent will shipments be sent? What quantities will be shipped each time? Will it be a fixed amount or variable?

f. What will be the return policy for the scissors? As there is not an existing agreement in place, how will service levels be defined and managed? How will any returned product be handled?

Fortunately, Connie's Cutting Corner is purchasing a product that CTC already makes. Although this creates a need to think through the respective transportation and distribution elements, CTC can likely follow the same pattern for how the product is managed and stored as it does for their other customers. The processes in place give them an example of how the product can be tracked, stored, and shipped. These procedures can then be modified as necessary to effectively manage the additional units that will be distributed to Connie's Cutting Corner.

In discussing the various responsibilities that make up the Logistics function, we have covered how product is managed once it leaves that factory floor, is stored, and moves between the various locations it needs to go on its way to consumers. We have also witnessed how critical it is for each of the Warehousing, Distribution, and Transportation activities to align with one another so that the right product is in the right place at the right time to effectively capture its intended target market. Without such commitment and dedication to reach the consumer, any efforts taken to meet evolving market demands would fall flat, never coming to fruition if they are not actually being delivered for broader consumption.

6

To summarize, in this chapter we have learned the following:

- *Ways that Inbound, Outbound, and Reverse Logistics work together to move materials*

- *What a warehouse does, and how to select the appropriate warehousing solution*

- *How WMS systems can be used to manage Warehouse Operations*

- *Ways to design a distribution approach that corresponds with the product being sold*

- *The advantages and disadvantages of different transportation modes*

- *How important the Logistics function is in ensuring products reach their target customers*

With the final step in the Supply Chain complete, product will reach the end customer and hopefully generate positive financial results for the company. As we have witnessed, this could not be achieved without constant collaboration along the way, and decision making that aligned with the company strategy.

We have asked many questions about how Supply Chain leaders can approach disruptive situations, and how they can pivot to meet demands in the market. In the remainder of this book we will look critically at how a company develops its strategy, to solidify why and how a business makes the decisions it does so that such a strategy can come to life.

6

This page is intentionally left blank

Chapter 7

Supply Chain Evolution

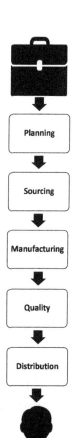

W e have witnessed why collaboration is important throughout the Supply Chain, as the activities of various functions integrate with one another to produce value-added products and services. What we have not discussed, however, is what drives the decisions that key decision leaders are making. In talking through CTC as an organization, we have addressed the concerns or considerations they may have in each area of the company when presented with new information or requirements. The answers to the questions posed, however, remain unclear. This was not done unintentionally.

The implied ambiguity was built into the story of CTC to demonstrate how decision making may morph and change over time. Although each functional area has defined responsibilities (planning, manufacturing, etc.) that they are held accountable for (which will remain unchanged), the specific response to a problem today may be drastically different from the response to the same problem a year from now. This would depend on the environment the business is in.

Take for example the Sourcing questions related to procuring the glue and plastic for the new type of scissors that CTC will make. Perhaps the market may be inexpensive for such products right now, but in one year's time prices could increase substantially. This is regularly witnessed in the Commodities market, where there is frequent volatility. As a company, you may anticipate such volatile price swings and give more thought to whether you want to enter into a long or short-term contract with a particular supplier. There are so many moving parts at play, however, that it is impossible, within the scope of this book, to define and analyze the exact conditions that CTC's business would be facing. As a result, there is some level of uncertainty around what the appropriate response may be without the additional required context.

The conditions that CTC would face can come from both external (market changes), and internal pressures, such as workforce availability or changes in company culture. That is not to say that real world businesses sit back and are left flat-footed, waiting to see what comes at them next. In reality, the opposite is true – companies predict and follow emerging trends, incorporate them into their overall strategy, and pivot their activities so that they remain viable. We will look at how strategies are developed and how they trickle down into the supply chain, as well as some emerging trends that are currently disrupting Supply Chains, throughout the course of this chapter. Although we cannot answer what direction CTC should take with the Supply Chain in their organization, we can look at the case of coffee chains in the real world to understand how companies approach similar questions to those that CTC is asking. This will solidify the principles we have discussed so far, and provide more perspective on what factors companies evaluate that drive Supply Chain decisions.

Strategy for Supply Chains

Strategy comes together with leadership and management to propel an organization forward. Although the term "strategy" may mean different things to different companies, it ultimately steers the company in a direction that will allow it to survive. This direction sends ripples through an organization, and thus dictates the underlying Supply Chain strategy that is the basis for Supply Chain decision making.

As we discussed in the introduction to this book, a company will chart a path for the direction that they want their business to take in order to remain competitive. The reason why strategy is so critical in a company's philosophy is because it serves as the basis for how a company will create and sustain its competitive advantage. Such a competitive advantage can be achieved through physical assets, such as natural resources or a global distribution system, or intangible assets, such as proprietary technology or knowledge from skilled employees.

Strategy development and execution is an ongoing challenge for organizations, because the market is continuously advancing and evolving in unpredictable ways. As such, strategies will change to meet unpredictable disruptions. We can look at the basis for how a company develops its overall strategy using a tool called Porter's 5 Forces. Michael Porter, who is a Professor at Harvard Business School, developed this framework to help think about the internal and external factors impacting the

7

environment of the company. The diagram below illustrates the forces that companies consider when developing their strategy.

Figure 7.1

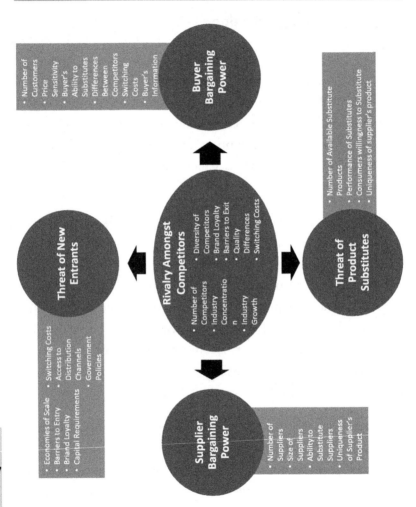

As you can tell, there is a wide range of competitive factors that a company would need to consider in determining where they should play within a given market. Porter's Five Forces is thus a great tool to analyze the competitive environment on a micro scale. To look internally at the potential of an organization, we can use a different tool that is known as the SWOT Analysis. This is more of a macro tool to demonstrate the strengths and opportunities that an organization can harness, while identifying the weaknesses and threats that need to be mitigated. We can see the framework for the SWOT analysis below.

Table 7.1

	Beneficial	*Harmful*
Internal Factors (Organizational Attributes)	*Strengths*	*Weaknesses*
External Factors (Environmental Attributes)	*Opportunities*	*Threats*

The combination of these two tools in the strategic planning process helps a company determine its position in the market and in what direction it should be steering the company. The tools can be used across service companies and those that make physical goods alike. They also span various industries, and can be used in a local or global context. Once a company chooses its direction, it is able to create its overall business strategy that will trickle down within the organization, driving the decisions that the company makes.

7

Let's practice putting these tools to use to witness how a strategy is formed. For our purposes, we can use the coffee industry as our reference point. There are various types of coffee offerings that exist, from at-home brewing beans and equipment, to subscription services, to boutique coffee shops, and coffee chains. The name that often comes to mind as a clear leader within the coffee industry is Starbucks, the coffee chain with more than 30,000 outlets around the globe. We can analyze their internal and external factors to see how they came to their strategy.

First, you will see how Porter's 5 Forces maps their competitive landscape. As we dig into the various areas of the market, new insights emerge.

7

Figure 7.2

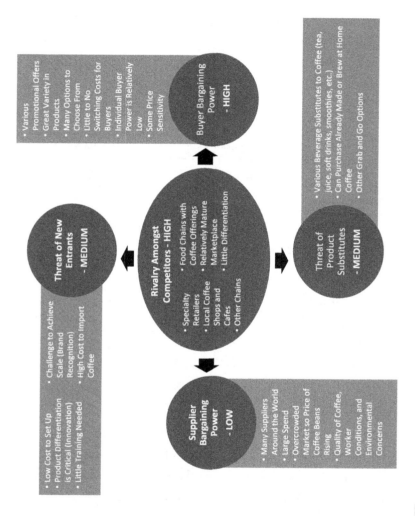

Although all areas within Porter's 5 Forces that we have analyzed for Starbucks tell us something about the industry, it is most critical to note that there are many competitors entering into the premium coffee space, which give buyers more options to choose. Although consumers may choose a different product aside from coffee, there is not much that Starbucks can do aside from offering those products as complements in their stores as well. If we look at the Starbucks' SWOT Analysis, this paints a very similar picture.

Table 7.2

	Beneficial	*Harmful*
Internal Factors (Organizational Attributes)	**Strengths:** • High Brand Recognition • Largest Coffee Chain in the World • Service with High Standard of Excellence	**Weaknesses:** • Competitor's Have Lower Prices • Strong US Presence, but Lower Worldwide • Buyers Unwilling to Wait in Long Queues for Coffee
External Factors (Environmental Attributes)	**Opportunities:** • Extend Supplier Network • Increase Product Offerings • Capture New Markets Through Distribution Channels	**Threats:** • Increasing Competition • Rising Coffee Bean Prices • Mature and Saturated Market in US

With everything we know about Starbucks' internal and external influences, we can then look at how they can craft their overall strategy. Through these tools, we can see what Starbucks' competitive advantage is, which includes the following:

1. Starbucks brand is well recognized and known around the world.

2. Product differentiation is key to align with changing consumer preferences and increased competition around the world.

It is no surprise, then, that we see these motives clearly articulated in Starbucks' mission statement which reads, "to inspire and nurture the human spirit – one person, one cup and one neighborhood at a time." This is Starbucks' statement to communicate their high-level corporate strategy to the rest of the world, including what business they will participate in, and how they aim to be competitive in that industry. This will be broken down one step further internally, to develop business-specific strategies for each type of product or market, such as the level of integration to target. This would drive specific motives and the decisions Starbucks makes, such as global expansion or product innovation. We can then separate out the business unit strategy. Let's take coffee drinks, for example (as opposed to food products, retail items, etc., which they also sell), into each functional area strategy within the company to understand the implications this would have, specifically for the Supply Chain.

- **Customer Strategy**   Increase customer loyalty and satisfaction. Enhance the sense of community in existing markets, and increase the market share in new ones.

- **Financial Strategy**   Grow revenue though more profitable products, reduce cost per unit and selling costs, and improve the utilization of existing assets.

- **Supply Chain Strategy**   Increase quality and process efficiency, increase coffee yield, increase long term relationships with suppliers, and decrease product cost and production time.

- **Learning and Development Strategy**   Attract and

7

retain good employees, increase employee motivation, and improve training quality.

With each sub-strategy, there will be key programs, allocated budgets, and desired benefits for each goal. When making decisions, leaders can thus refer to these directions and ask, "Does this action align with our strategy?" as a general rule of thumb. If the answer is no, typically the action should not be taken. This could apply to anything from a distribution strategy around warehousing and transportation elements to quality strategies relating to program development and implementation. Let's look at a few scenarios within the Supply Chain for Starbucks and determine what actions would, and would not, align with the company's objectives.

1. *Starbucks has been approached about a new factory with the latest technology that would reduce the lead time for processing its coffee beans. Should it buy the new factory?*

   NO. Even with the little information provided, we know that this conflicts with the desire to increase their process efficiency and decrease product cost. This scenario is a bit tricky because although the new factory would decrease the time for production, it would jeopardize the other key goals of the Supply Chain strategy by increasing the product cost. It also conflicts with an element of the Financial Strategy – to increase the utilization of existing assets. Essentially, achieving one element of the Supply Chain strategy cannot come at the expense of another.

2. *Starbucks' suppliers for coffee beans have hinted at the posibility of a long-term purchase agreement with fixed-price commitments. Should Starbucks enter into the pur-*

7

chase contract?

> YES. We know that the price of coffee beans is increasing. Coffee is a core area of Starbucks' business, and they will not move out of the coffee industry any time soon. If they are able to work with their suppliers to lock in an advantageous purchase price (which given their scale and purchase volume would be possible), this would achieve the goal of enhancing long-term relationships with the suppliers they are already using. They may even get higher quality beans and preferential treatment over other buyers as the relationship grows over time.

3. Due to high labor costs in the US where Starbucks completes the roasting process for their coffee beans, there have been questions around outsourcing this step to other countries where the beans are grown, before shipping them to Starbucks' distribution centers. Should Starbucks outsource this step in the Supply Chain?

> NO. Close control over the roasting process is required to ensure that the coffee from Starbucks tastes the same in all of its retail locations. By giving up ownership of this process, the company may jeopardize the quality of their coffee. In addition, it may decrease coffee yields from inexperienced roasting facilities, and actually increase product cost. It may also jeopardize the efficiency of the existing distribution centers and transportation network that the company has in place.

7

4. Increasing environmental concerns have raised question about sustainable coffee production, prompting Starbucks to purchase Fair Trade Certified coffee beans and assist with environmental conservation. Should Starbucks go a step

> further to implement programs around biodiversity and cultivation methods?
>
> YES. Aside from the Corporate Social Responsibility measures the company has already taken, getting involved with coffee growing and harvesting programs may result in higher quality beans that result in higher yields, or foster new areas of innovation. This may also increase demand for Starbucks coffee across consumers with environmental concerns, keeping pace with consumer preferences.

Each of these decisions requires careful consideration and alignment with the company's existing Supply Chain Strategy and assets in place. Answers to questions like these, as well as countless others, helps to form the Supply Chain Design that serves as the structure for the supply chain within the company. The overall design takes into account the locations and capabilities of individual facilities, which products will be stored where, how they will be transported, and any information systems that might be used to help them function with one another. These decisions must be made with caution, however, because they are meant for long-term implementations and would likely be expensive to reverse. At the core, the Supply Chain Design should be based on flexibility, strong leadership, a commitment to continuous improvement, and business function collaboration in order to be successful.

7

With an understanding of how a company develops its strategy and makes decisions within the Supply Chain to support said strategy, you should now have a clear idea of how CTC may behave given the various questions we posed about their business activities throughout the book. As many of the questions were a result of external developments in the market, it is important to understand some of the key trends impacting supply chains. We will learn what these trends are and how they may continue to evolve, in the next section.

Disruptive Trends

Supply Chains have evolved and adapted over time in response to factors out of their traditional scope. Although the functions that encompass Supply Chain Operations have existed over a long period of time, especially with the emergence of the assembly line, the field did not gain prevalence until the 1990s. This was due partially to the fact that large-scale changes were needed in the way products were produced, with a focus on cost reduction, Japanese management styles, and specialization through downsizing. At the start of the 21st century, there were further developments as the business environment as well as technological enhancements changed the way companies conducted their operations. We can look at some of these trends and how they ultimately have disrupted Supply Chains in the past, and will continue to do so going forward.

Lower Communication Costs

As Supply Chains have developed, there is a larger degree of complexity that is inherent in the vast network of a company's operations. In order to manage such involved systems, greater coordination is required. A big part of this coordination is in regard to information flow between different parties within the organization, external service providers, suppliers, and customers. Internet-based applications have emerged that create col-

7

laborative systems to support business activities such as remote meetings, data availability and storage, and workflow management and approvals. These applications help to reduce transaction costs that were historically very high in the absence of such systems.

Business Process Integration

The ability of more systems to talk to one another has provided the means for deeper integration, where actions of individual functions within a company are imbedded into key processes within the Supply Chain. As such, there is business collaboration across product development, customers, suppliers, and business partners using shared information and common systems within organizations. Perhaps the two most noteworthy developments for business process integration include Electronic Data Interchange (EDI) and Enterprise Resource Planning (ERP) systems. EDI allows companies to electronically communicate information that would otherwise need to be sent on paper. This would include things like purchase orders or invoices that can be sent from one computer to another between either internal business partners or external customers, using a standard electronic format. ERP systems, on the other hand, integrate the activities of a company's various functions and applications into one central system, increasing visibility of information across the whole organization, and even on occasion, with external business partners. Essentially, ERP serves as a central database that multiple business units are able to access to view data and input the data generated by their functions.

With this level of data integration, there is increased value added to businesses, as well as cost reduction within the Supply Chain. These are often derived from activities such as demand management, customer service management, product development, commercialization, order fulfillment, and customer relationship management being handled electronically. Ultimately, this drives collaboration, better information flow, and more timely feedback from the market. It may even lead to vertical integration where a company has control over the entire supply chain of a product from supply of raw materials through some stage of distribution.

Globalization

Starting in the late 1980s there was a push by organizations to include global sources into the core of their business activities. This also spurred new business relationships, such as joint ventures, multinational companies, and global partnerships. Improvements in communication, and the drop in the cost to communicate globally have been key drivers behind the way businesses are managed and carry out their transactions. As companies have expanded their businesses beyond domestic markets, for both their operational activities as well as to reach new customers, there has been a dramatic impact on how Supply Chains operate.

With global customers and suppliers, the invoicing, souring, manufacturing, distribution, and customer returns processes have all needed to adapt. For example, if products that were traditionally delivered from a domestic supplier are now sourced from businesses internationally, this would increase the lead time for getting the product, as it would take longer for cross border transportation, the customs clearance process, and onward transportation to the warehouse or manufacturing site where it would be used. This would have serious implications for the planning process, as well as the Quality function, which

7

may need to implement additional programs or measures to ensure the safety and quality of inbound foreign products.

This further drives the need to build flexibility into the Supply Chain in order to adapt to an international business environment. Rapid globalization drives the need for the right Supply Chain design that can operate in a cost-effective manner. This ties back to the overall Supply Chain strategy in order to determine where to locate various facilities, their capacities, and what products they will handle. Decisions around distribution and outsourcing, as well as system integrations, are ever more critical is assigning ownership to activities both inside and outside of the organization. Although globalization has created challenges for the Supply Chain function, ultimately its emergence has added value, reduced sourcing costs, and increased competitive advantages for many organizations.

Trade, Trade Agreements, and Tariffs

In line with globalization, Trade has increased across borders, and with such increase, trade policies have needed to develop as well. There have been a number of questions raised recently around the North American Free Trade Agreement (NAFTA) and the Trans-Pacific Partnership (TPP), that were developed among a number of trade arrangements to support the increase in cross-border trade as a result of global expansion. Such agreements are heavily impacted by tariffs and global sanctions, which may spur additional negotiations. Tariffs, in particular on goods like steel and aluminum can dramatically impact the Supply Chains that are supported by those products from a Sourcing standpoint. Questions around customs clearance processes and production shutdown risks are potential threats that come with a decrease in traded goods. When established trade patterns and sources of supply are jeopardized, the previous efforts to globalize operations may be undone. A level of uncertainty may also prompt organizations to go back to the drawing board and develop mitigation measures, as well as reevaluate their global strategy for the Supply Chain.

Robotics

In the 21st century, robotics within the Supply Chain extends beyond the industrial manufacturing applications introduced by GM in the 1960s. Robotics technology, such as Artificial Intelligence (AI) allows for similar physical robots, but with decision making power, such as how to navigate an obstruction in a distribution center. The Internet of Things (IoT) is another robotics technology with Supply Chain implications, as it can capture and communicate data of an existing operation in real time, whether that be in a service activity, such as tracking a bus route, or for physical products, such as to track and signal inventory levels. A final application, the Cloud, is being used for robotics control, where an operator can correct the actions or resolve any issues of a robot from a remote location.

Although there are many applications for physical robots for things like warehousing such as those implemented by Amazon's fulfillment process (which historically has been very manual for most companies), the use of digital robots has seen far greater developments. Technology such as ERP systems now allows companies to take imputed data and automate some business actions such as transaction processing and records maintenance through Robotic Process Automation (RPA). Overall, the business case for companies to implement robotics applications has evolved over time, and now includes reduced cost, higher efficiency, and greater productivity. These benefits are achieved

7

primarily through greater speed and higher flexibility for an organization.

Data Analytics

The emergence of data management and availability has supported the rise of the Data Analytics field, which has many implications for Supply Chain decision making. With more insight into historical events and patterns, there is less reliance on human judgment when, instead, predictive analytics can be used to understand future outcomes, particularly in relation to demand. Actions taken within the Planning, Sourcing, and Logistics functions of an organization can now be supported with data to more accurately gauge the efficiency of how products move and are transformed in the Supply Chain. This also helps to mitigate negative events that may arise in the future, and identify new areas of opportunity or improvement for businesses.

Digitalization

The Logistics function within the Supply Chain has seen the greatest impact from the emergence of digitalization. What digitalization does is combine technology solutions with physical assets by converting them into a form that can be processed by a computer. There are strong overlaps of digitalization with the emergence of the Internet of Things (IoT) as a new form of robotics. By going digital, the Logistics function is able to respond with greater speed and resiliency to changes that are happening in the Supply Chain. This usually helps with inventory management, fleet optimization, and better management of inventory sitting in the company's warehouses. Businesses can also increase customer responsiveness by leveraging various digital

7

technologies like chat bots, e-mails, social media, and text messaging. In order to harness these benefits, however, a company cannot simply add in digital technology; rather, it must redesign the supply chain strategy to fit with digital systems.

Omni Channel Retailing

Customers are becoming increasingly more demanding about the products they want and how they want to purchase them in the retail industry. Whether through a mobile app, online, or in a store, customers expect the same experience and level of customer service when buying a company's product. As a result, many companies are looking to flexibility and cost optimization in order to fulfill such promises to their target market. This often creates challenges for inventory management, where process modifications are needed. For example, a product may be available via one channel (let's say online), but is unavailable in another (say in the store). Customer frustration and a loss of sales may result from this instance. Common solutions are to look for ways to gain efficiencies and to put the right systems in place to track and manage inventory. Solutions could also involve removing silos between the various selling outlets by using common warehouse space to fulfill both online and in-store orders, for example. Although this trend is specific to the retail industry, it is expected to play a larger role in how Supply Chains are designed in the future, as they will have to accommodate such changes in purchasing behavior regardless of whether a retailer is a direct customer or a downstream seller of a company's products.

7

Throughout this chapter, we have looked at the various environmental influences on a company's Supply Chain and how it may respond as a result. We evaluated how an organization's corporate strategy is developed, which would then filter down to impact the broader Supply Chain strategy. We have also looked at some of the external trends and market factors that would not only influence a company's strategy, but its decision making about modifications within the Supply Chain network. In conclusion, this chapter should provide you with more perspective on how Supply Chains are built and enhanced, and how they evolve to meet changing market conditions.

7

Chapter **8**

Supply Chain in the Modern World

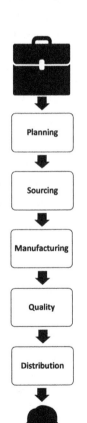

Up to this point, we have discussed Supply Chain Operations under a management context – the area where this field was born. That is not to say there aren't endless other applications and areas of our daily lives where we can see the activities of the Supply Chain at work. There are countless processes that we do on a day-to-day basis that we may not even realize are mirrored by the Supply Chain functions we have discussed in this book. If you think of yourself as the epicenter of interconnected Supply Chains, you will start to see what a valuable role this field plays in ensuring we operate smoothly.

Practical Applications

Instead of looking at Supply Chain uses for the corporate world, let's look at some of the more human elements of Supply Chain activities. Take your weekend for example

– there are various cases where there is a Supply Chain impact, and it's when managed correctly, a number of benefits are realized. To put this into perspective, let's walk through a hypothetical day.

Morning Routine

When you first wake up, you may roll over and check your phone for updates, news, and any incoming messages. Perhaps you have a text message from your siblings about getting a birthday present for your mom. This may require you to decide how much you want to spend on the gift, what you want to buy, who will buy it, and where you will get it. These are all planning steps that require you to allocate your resources, which in this case are time and money. You may also look at your calendar to see what important meetings and appointments you have coming up. These would have been set in advance based on your current priorities and basic needs. If any appointments have changed, or cannot be completed within the day, you will need to allocate time to complete them in the future. Maybe you needed to mail a letter, but just realized you don't have any stamps and the post office is closed that day. You would need to schedule time to get the stamps and then mail the letter at a later date. These are all prime examples of the planning process, all before you have gotten out of bed.

Next you get ready to head off for the day. When brushing your teeth, taking a shower, shaving, or styling your hair, there are a number of products that you may use. Each of these needed to be purchased in the past to ensure that there was an ample amount available for your use when you needed them. This includes a certain element of planning as well, but also is impacted by procurement. How you buy these products, whether it be

8

online where they are delivered to your house, or by physically driving to a store to purchase them, has resource implications. You need to make a decision on the retailer where you would like to purchase them. Perhaps getting them delivered to your house is more convenient; however, if you are already in a big-box store purchasing other goods, it may not make sense to pay the shipping price to have them delivered when you can just buy them right there. Alternatively, you may choose to participate in a subscription service where these items are delivered on a consistent basis, but you may be less familiar with the products you are getting, accepting some level of risk in doing so. There are also considerations from a cost perspective. Perhaps you have sensitive teeth, and are willing to pay more for special toothpaste. On the flip side, you may care less about your hairstyle, and buy inexpensive gel just to meet its basic functionality. Certain stores may offer discounts on the products you buy as well, causing you to shop in their establishments over other retailers. All of these decisions are trade-offs between cost versus quality of the items that you procure.

Daytime Activities

Now that you are ready for the day, you make a to-do list based on the activities and appointments set out in your calendar for that particular day. You also may look at what you have coming up during the week, so that you have adequate lead time to prepare for any special events. For the day's tasks, perhaps you are having friends over for dinner in the evening, so you need to stop at the store to pick up some supplies. You also may plan to go to the gym before going home to prepare for your evening of hosting. Your brother has asked you to purchase your mother's birthday present by one week from today, so perhaps you will leave that task to be accomplished later in the week

8

when you are less busy.

First you decide to stop at your gym, where you have signed a year-long service contract that functions as your membership. The gym has a finite number of machines, so if you are going during peak hours when there is greater demand, it could be very crowded. This may be less efficient as you will have to spend time waiting for equipment between exercises. Fortunately, you chose a very sophisticated, high-end gym that gives you access to an app that shows you how busy the gym is at any given time. This gym also offers fitness classes that you could sign up for in advance, to ensure you get a spot in a particular class despite its limited capacity for participants. Afterwards, you may evaluate if the class met your expectations. Of course, because this gym ensures the highest quality services, such as personal trainers, customized fitness plans, and clean, well-equipped locker rooms, your membership comes at a higher price. This may encourage you to go more often to get the most value out of what you are purchasing, increasing your membership yield. Your trip to the gym has demonstrated many aspects of both manufacturing and Supply Chain in a service function.

With the gym out of the way, it is time to go to the store to get the supplies for your dinner party, including the ingredients for the dinner itself. Perhaps you have promised your friends that you would make your grandma's famous spaghetti recipe. This would require you to buy tomatoes, a variety of spices, Italian sausage, any secret ingredients, and spaghetti noodles. You may also choose to buy bread and ingredients for a salad to go along with it, as well as a few bottles of wine. The quantities of the items that you buy will depend on the number of guests you are having, as well as what ratio of ingredients your grandma's recipe calls for. The recipe serves as both your Bill of Materials,

8

as it tells you how much of any one item is required to make your end product, spaghetti, and your Process, as it tells you the steps for combining ingredients to make the sauce and stipulates cook times and temperatures for how it will be prepared. Given that the star of your dinner is the spaghetti, you may choose to simply buy some of the other complementary items, such as a pre-made salad, instead of making them yourself, given you have only so much time before your guests will arrive. You will also need to consider what items you already have in inventory at home, so that you do not purchase something that is already occupying your cupboard space. In addition to the food items, you will also need to consider any equipment you need, such as pots and pans, as well as tools, like a spatula for mixing the sauce itself. Then there are indirect items that will support your dinner, such as plates, cups, and napkins, that are necessary to enjoy your homemade spaghetti.

With many decisions made around the dinner you will serve, and with the corresponding purchases made, you then return home to start preparing. As you are about to walk in your front door, your neighbors call over to say hello. After chatting about weekend plans, you decide to invite them over to join in your dinner party, to which they happily agree, and they offer to bring dessert, an item not addressed on your current menu, so their contribution comes as a relief. After sorting out your groceries and prepping the supplies needed to make your sauce, you realize that your neighbor is a vegetarian. You hadn't planned for this, and it poses a problem for your sauce that contains Italian sausage. A simple solution would be to leave the sausage out; however, you had promised your friends that they would finally get to try the famous recipe. Alternatively, you could make two separate batches, one that is smaller without sausage added, and a larger amount for the rest of your guests.

8

This second option would take a bit more time, greater coordination, and be dependent on whether you have enough of the various ingredients on hand. It may also require you to learn a new meat-free recipe, or find ways to modify the existing one so that it still tastes good without the meat flavor. The outcome of such flexibility, however, would be that you could please the demands of the various consumers you are serving, so you decide to take that route.

Evening

With an hour left before your guests arrive, and your cooking well underway, you may start to see if you have allocated enough time for each step in preparing for your dinner as well as enough time for you to set the table and change your clothes. You start by using a thermometer to check the temperature of your different sauces to gauge if they need to cook longer, or are overdone and to ensure they reach your grandma's quality standards. When baking your bread, you have only enough space for one loaf in your oven, even though you need to bake two. You are constrained by the temperature and space capacity of your oven, where the first loaf must finish before you can start baking the second. When focusing on your sauce and bread, you forgot about the boiling noodles! They are now overcooked, and too sticky to serve. In throwing them away, you need to dip into your noodle reserves to make a new pot. Fortunately, one of your friends has offered to come over early to help you set up, allowing you to outsource some of your non-core tasks such as setting the table, pulling out extra chairs, and filling the water glasses. Your production process may not have been completely smooth, but you were able to adapt and put out fires as they came up.

8

As your guests are about to arrive, you put the final touches on your food just in time. This ensures that you are able to greet them as they arrive and you don't keep them waiting too long before dinner is served, solidifying your good hosting status. After much time chatting, drinking, and settling in, it is time for your dinner to be served. To ensure that once the spaghetti was finished it would not get cold before serving, you kept it in its original cooking pot at a very low heat setting. You now transfer the sauces and noodles onto a serving dish, clearly signaling which sauce has meat and which doesn't. As the bread is sliced and brought to the table along with the salad, your meal is complete. With full stomachs, your guests voice their satisfaction with the dinner you offered them, raving about your grandma's recipe. You found the sauce to be a bit salty, which signals a continuous improvement effort that can be implemented the next time you make it.

After your guests depart for the night, you realize your kitchen looks like a disaster, given your frantic cooking to get your dinner finished in time. You then proceed to wash all of your plates, pots, pans, utensils, and serving dishes to be put away. Each has a particular place that it is stored to ensure your kitchen remains organized and you are able to find these items at a later time. Perhaps you take out the trash and throw any empty wine bottles in the recycling to ensure that there is no clutter that piles up in your kitchen and that the area remains clean. With your kitchen's original condition back in order, you carry out your evening routine to get ready for bed much like you did in the morning. After a long day, you reflect on the various processes, purchases, verifications, and plans that you carried out within the span of a short period of time, many of which will be carried out again tomorrow.

8

This series of events shows how Supply Chain decisions don't necessarily need to be complex. It also demonstrates how Supply Chain Operations are carried out every day, in ways that we don't even realize. Take the items purchased at the grocery store, for example. The company providing spices would have had to anticipate your demand for them and deliver them to the store far before you ever even invited your friends over for dinner. Similarly, in the instance of going to a fitness class, the gym would have had to formulate a class schedule and ensure there is an instructor available to teach the class before you even signed up. These nuances of business are the exact reason why Supply Chain is playing an ever more critical role in how we live our lives, by anticipating our needs and delivering products and services that meet them. As we develop different preferences for greater product availability, digital purchasing, or increased convenience, the Supply Chain is ultimately what will support this. Business applications aside, the Supply Chain ensures we can make a nice meal to share with our closest confidants, or find the perfect birthday present for a parent, providing great personal value.

Concluding Thoughts

Throughout the course of this book, we set out to get a better understanding of the Supply Chain Operations field and why it matters to us. We looked at each area that supports the Supply Chain function, including Planning, Sourcing, Manufacturing, Quality, and Logistics to understand the critical role that each plays in delivering products that meet customers' needs and standards. We also saw how the areas outside the Supply Chain, such as Research and Development, Sales, and Marketing interact with these functions and impact the products that the com-

8

pany sells to its target market. This overview has provided an understanding of what employees in each of these functions of the business are responsible for, and what decisions they need to make. Whether it be taking purchase orders or managing inventory, each department has a key role that it plays, and particular systems that need to integrate and talk with one another. By looking at how a company develops its strategy, we can see how a business allocates resources and makes such business decisions, based on both internal and external environmental factors and disruptive trends.

This comprehensive look at the field of Supply Chain Operations should give you a broad understanding of the topic and the ability to point out Supply Chain applications in your daily life. By looking at the hypothetical company, Cut the Cord Scissors Company, which we referred to as CTC, you could start to see how changes in customer preferences would impact the way a business would operate. By looking at the strategy development example for Starbucks, we could see some actual decisions that would be made in the Supply Chain to meet the demands of the market, while maintaining a competitive advantage and thus remaining a relevant coffee provider. Finally, by playing out a typical day that a consumer may face, we can start to see the importance that Supply Chain tasks play in making our lives easier. As we are all consumers of something, whether it be services or physical goods, we must pay attention to the role of the Supply Chain, as it will continue to evolve and grow in the face of emerging trends in technology, communication, and global business practices. Given this importance, we hope you are equipped with the knowledge and awareness to capture the benefits that will continue to emerge in a world rich with Supply Chains.

8

NOTES

Made in the USA
Middletown, DE
11 November 2021

51871624R00106